Kristin~ Thanks for all your
help ~ You _are_ the greatest!

Michael Peronzier

Good Kids

the story of ArtWorks

Michael Peringer

ISBN: 978-1-59404-033-7
LCCN: 2007927087

Printed in the United States of America

Editor: Carole Glickfeld
Illustrator/Photographer: Laura Harper
Author Photographer: Rick Jay
Design: Soundview Design Studio

SODO Publishing
an imprint of
Quality Code Publishing
2100 Westlake Avenue North, Suite 106
Seattle, Washington 98109
800-328-4348
www.qcode.us

There is nothing more beautiful than
the truth of real existence.

August Rodin

Acknowledgments

W here to begin? To take on a task like this requires, actually demands, the support of many individuals and organizations: sponsors, several criminal justice-related agencies including the Seattle Police Department and King County Superior Court Juvenile Division; good folks like Verne Rainey and Judge Patricia Clark; and, obviously, ArtWorks itself, as well as the many youth groups participating in this ten-year labor of love.

I am also grateful for the support of the remarkable kids who were part of ArtWorks and "graduated," and who are now experiencing productive and meaningful lives.

My thanks to the young authors who helped me with the stories in this book. These include three of my granddaughters, Michaela Peringer and Sarah and Samantha Youssefi. Thanks to Christen Heye, Sarah's friend, and the incredible help I received from my daughter, Amanda Smith. Simply put, without their able assistance, there would not be a book.

The unparalleled support of Jim Diers, Seattle's first Director of the Department of Neighborhoods, was critical to the program's success.

Without the loyalty and passion of the executive directors, artists, mentors, other staffers and the literally hundreds of volunteers, ArtWorks would simply not exist.

Many kudos to our current Executive Director, Laura Harper, and her able assistants, Jesse, Derek and Jenny. I will never forget their outstanding service. And Laura's illustrations for this book are terrific.

Thanks to the Board of Directors of the SODO (South of Downtown) Business Association and to my employers, Rick and Ron Jay, of Process Heating Company, who allowed me to spend valuable time nurturing this program. Also thanks to Rick Jay for his photographic skills in making me look good.

No acknowledgments would be complete without mentioning the several consultants with whom we have worked over the years, including Leslie Rankin and Jeanne Krikawa. The same goes for Anne Jay who has kept me on time for most of my many daily meetings.

Thanks also go to Kristen Morris and Carole Glickfeld, the book's publisher and editor, respectively, for their expertise and for keeping me going in the right direction.

And, my wife, Shirley, who has put up with my ramblings these past years, not to mention my grumpiness about matters and frustrations that seem to go with the territory of non-profit organizations.

To all, I can only say, you will be in my heart forever.

Introduction

Good Kids is the story of ArtWorks, a non-profit corporation that has enabled over five thousand at-risk youthful offenders to serve their "sentence" in a rigorous art program, rather than in detention. Initiated in 1995 in Seattle, Washington, by the SODO (South of Downtown) Business Association, ArtWorks has not only enhanced the city's uniqueness through the creation of thousands of public murals, it has sought to re-direct the lives of teenagers who have taken a wrong turn in their journey to adulthood.

Good Kids tries to illuminate the history and administration of a program that continues to change lives for the better. The narratives are based on true outcomes and are inspired by real teenagers—however, they are composites and are not based on any one individual youth. Jamaal's story, for example, is a composite of a typical youth offender and what he encounters along the way, from his arrest, to his sentencing, to his time at ArtWorks.

I sincerely hope what follows will plant seeds that will grow into many more positive programs. My goal is to help at-risk youth, as well as their parents and the law enforcement officials who are bravely trying to cope with increasing instances of juvenile crime in cities and suburbs throughout the United States.

Mike Peringer

Foreword

One of the most intractable problems faced by the SODO (south of downtown) community was the E-3 Busway, which is lined by the back sides of warehouses along its entire two-mile route through this industrial district. The expansive walls were completely covered with graffiti. Used condoms, needles and piles of other trash on either side of the road added to the blight and bore evidence of the public safety problems that spilled over into the rest of the district. This is the scene that greeted sixteen thousand commuters as they entered Seattle each day and it was the last thing they saw as they left the city.

Although he works as marketing director for a heating equipment company in Seattle's SODO industrial area, Mike Peringer's passion is building community. He serves as president of the SODO Business Association, chair of the East Precinct Crime Council, and in many other volunteer capacities with less glorious titles, such as trash collector. Mike is one of those good people who make community possible.

Part of his strength is that he is an effective advocate. Mike and his organizations are a force to be reckoned with. They hold police, politicians, and other public servants accountable. Mike does his homework and works respectfully with government officials, but he is determined and won't take "no" or excuses for an answer.

Mike and his cohorts persuaded city officials to conduct more enforcement activity in the corridor, but they didn't stop there. They understood that government couldn't resolve the problem alone and that the community had to assume some responsibility of its own. They knew that their neighborhood wasn't just a place with great needs but a community of people with tremendous untapped resources.

Mike's story demonstrates the power of focusing on assets and individuals rather than needs and labels. Where most people saw graffiti-covered walls, Mike saw a canvass for an urban art corridor. Mike believed that young people who had been labeled "at risk" were individuals whose energy and creativity could be utilized to create beautiful murals. He also tapped the assets of local businesses, whether it was the paint company for their expertise and supplies, the district's many employees for volunteers, or Starbucks' headquarters for coffee to fuel the work parties.

The results were extraordinary. The first work party resulted in the removal of thirty tons of trash. The blighted corridor was transformed into an outdoor art gallery featuring more than fifty spectacular murals. Most of the murals were painted by young people who had been convicted of crimes such as defacing property with graffiti. As they painted, the youth were taught work and life skills by their mentors in ArtWorks. The young people did not re-offend while engaged in ArtWorks, so the summer mural project grew to become a year-round program creating banners as well as hundreds of plywood murals for construction sites throughout the city. Close to five thousand young people have benefited from the program over its first ten years.

Good Kids is also about good government. Local governments everywhere are facing a crisis because their revenues aren't keeping pace with the increasingly complex social issues and because people are thinking of themselves as taxpayers rather than citizens. A new paradigm is needed in which government goes beyond processes of citizen participation to programs of community empowerment. Rather than involve citizens in government initiatives, government must learn to support community initiatives; this is the basis for effective partnerships. In the case of ArtWorks, it was the King County Court, Seattle Public Utilities, and the Department of Neighborhoods that supported the community's initiative. Mike's story illustrates the power of such partnerships as government and community work together to accomplish what neither could do on their own.

The Urban Art Corridor is one of more than three thousand community-initiated projects that have been supported by the City of Seattle's Neighborhood Matching Fund. Tens of thousands of citizen volunteers have participated in these projects, demonstrating that Mike Peringer is not alone in caring about community. People will get involved when they are given the opportunity to utilize their gifts to achieve results around issues important to them.

Mike's book offers sound advice (be persistent, build relationships, etc.) that will be helpful to other activists no matter what issue they are confronting. More importantly, it provides the inspiration that will motivate more people to get involved in their communities. Much of the inspiration comes in the form of stories, such as one about elementary school students, gang members, and elders who supported one another in creating a mural; or one about two hundred fifty youth who completed twelve murals in one day. True to Mike's convictions, he called on young people to write powerful stories in his book illustrating the enormous challenges faced by so many youth and the way in which ArtWorks empowers them to be good kids.

Mike Peringer understands the potential power of community assets—youth, elders, businesses, associations, institutions, and stories. Moreover, he acts on his understanding. Be like Mike!

Mike Peringer's modesty is part of what makes him so effective. If I, rather than Mike, had written this book, it would have been entitled: Good Man.

Jim Diers

table of Contents

jamaal

"Get over here, Jamaal…NOW! You know the routine. It's not like you haven't been here before," the guard bellowed in his best drill instructor voice.

Jamaal shuffled over to the designated area of the King County Juvenile Detention Center, so familiar to him. It was here that he had been photographed, fingerprinted and assigned a number only a year earlier, the result of his arrest for drug dealing. So, yes, he knew the drill.

Actually he sort of liked Officer Kindly, as Jamaal called him. Despite his gruff exterior, he treated Jamaal with a certain amount of respect, or so Jamaal thought. Jamaal knew he didn't mean it as he winked at him. "What were you thinking, kid?" Officer Kindly said, as Jamaal approached the veteran guard. "The next time, and it will be all over. Even our lenient judge won't let you go. You'll be looking at real time, Jamaal. Don't let us down, kid."

With that brief lecture behind him, Jamaal slowly walked to his "dorm room," his home away from home for the next few days. At least he hoped it would only be for a few days.

Jamaal opened the door only to be confronted by his already assigned roommate, a rather large teenager, black like himself, who,

Jamaal later discovered, had also assaulted a guy on the street who was giving him "a bad time." In Jamaal's case the "victim" turned out to be an undercover Seattle cop. Because Jamaal was much larger than the Seattle Police Department rookie, he got the best of him until help arrived. Jamaal didn't know what his victim looked like after he was through with him. He didn't want to know.

Some of the rooms in the Center housed a single teen and Jamaal wondered if he should ask for a transfer. But, he didn't. Jamaal figured that if this guy knew he made that request, well, he didn't want to think about the outcome. Because this guy was sitting on the lower bunk, his turf, Jamaal put his duffle bag on the upper one.

All he had to do now was wait for his turn before the judge. He hoped it would be sooner rather than later, under the circumstances, circumstances beyond his control.

First, Jamaal would be assigned a public defender (PD) who would go through the motions of justice, knowing all along his "client" would be found guilty of this latest burglary attempt, the one that obviously failed. Yes, he knew the drill.

Within hours of his newfound residency Jamaal would confer with his PD on a strategy to keep him out of prison for this second offense. Jamaal would tell him (or her if he was lucky) the circumstances relating to his attempt to pick up a little cash necessary to keep going. He hadn't realized that the owner was home. Jamaal thought he had gone to work on the swing shift at the warehouse where he served as a security guard, but he had forgotten his lunch. He caught Jamaal, whom he knew from the neighborhood, wandering outside the house with a bicycle in his search for valuables. Even though Jamaal managed to leave, it was only a matter of time till he was confronted by two of Seattle's finest.

And, so, here he was, ready to get his sentence in a day or two. The question of guilt or innocence was not even considered.

After what seemed like hours of sitting with Teddy, not Ted, but Teddy, Jamaal's new roommate, awaiting the call to make his way down the hallway to the courtroom, the door swung open. Officer Kindly entered, asking, no, ordering Jamaal to follow him, which he gladly did.

During the brief walk, he wondered what he would say. He knew he was guilty and that he was now a two-time loser and he hadn't yet reached his sixteenth birthday. The only unknown was the sentence.

Jamaal had been born at home, the third of what was to become a family of six kids. He had two older brothers and later, three younger sisters. One of them, Latisha, was born about ten months after Jamaal. They were quite close, even best friends, according to her.

Latisha had been in the courtroom the last time he was caught and sentenced to three months of "house arrest" for burglary of the neighbors' house where he had been caught in the act, much like this time. He was sentenced to his parents' custody. He completed those three months with ease and was free again, at least for a while.

He attended the local high school sporadically. He was a sophomore, or at least he thought he was. He actually preferred hanging out with the usual bunch from the neighborhood who looked for any excuse not to attend classes. They'd all meet after school started and wander the streets of the neighborhood hour after hour. More often than not, day after day, as well.

The public schools in Seattle were pretty lax when it came to kids like Jamaal. He was convinced the school administrators didn't know whether or not he was there sitting in that hot, overcrowded classroom. And, what's more, he didn't care if they did or didn't. So, he hung out nearly every day. Sometimes the kids would hop in one of the guys' cars and just drive around the Emerald City. Sometimes the kids would talk someone into buying them some beer at their nearby convenience store. Other times they would take a bus, the number 7, for the fifteen-minute ride downtown. There they could meet up with other street kids, maybe do a little panhandling if they felt like it. Seattle had this weird tolerance policy when it came to begging on the streets: It was okay, it seemed, as long as they didn't sit down while doing it. There was never a shortage of kids to hang out with. They seemed to be all over the city.

Jamaal's father worked in the warehouse of the local Safeway market, a pretty good job for a guy who had quit grade school. His mother worked at the local deli making a minimum wage for long, irregular hours, but she was able to bring home some pretty good food from time to time to feed her six kids, or at least, those who were home when it was suppertime. Together, the parents could barely keep enough food on the table in the small, two-bedroom house to sustain a family of eight, not to mention keeping clothes on their backs. The other siblings, particularly the older ones, didn't get into the same type of trouble that continually came Jamaal's way. Jamaal wanted more than any of them would offer, including his parents.

So he went after what he thought would be a better life in the only way he knew, burglary, his crime of choice.

Before his fourteenth birthday, Jamaal had, as he would later tell the probation counselor, broken into at least two dozen homes before being caught. Since the homes were in a rather poor neighborhood, his cash take was generally pretty small.

Sometimes he would be "blanked," not netting anything for the high degree of risk he experienced. But, he managed to get by. He was getting frustrated, though, and longed to have enough to last more than a few days or weeks. He was thinking of taking his efforts to yet another level soon, like robbing convenience stores or gas stations. All this was in his mind the night he was caught, the night his life would change forever.

Juvenile offenses are categorized by level of severity from A through E. Level A could be murder or arson, for example. Level

B includes burglary. C includes robbery, forgery, possession of stolen property, taking motor vehicles without permission. D includes drug possession with intent to distribute or sell as well as possession of burglary tools; eluding police; attempted motor theft. E includes criminal trespass, disorderly conduct or malicious mischief (vandalism, graffiti). Jamaal pleaded guilty to a level C possession of stolen property and criminal trespass.

There are over 5,000 youth arrested each year in King County, Washington with approximately 4,000 cases filed in juvenile court. The cost of incarceration can be over $200 per day, an annual expense to taxpayers of over $1,000,000 each and every year. In addition, some 1,200 are placed on probation at a terrific dollar savings, but with no assurance of the outcome. Re-offenses tend to be commonplace with at-risk youths. Jamaal's situation was more the norm than not.

The King County, Washington criminal justice system begins with over fifty judges. There are four assigned to the Juvenile Court, about two miles from the downtown King County Courthouse. This facility contains the Juvenile Detention Center and Superior Court, whose judges can request assignment to the Juvenile Division. They operate under the jurisdiction of a presiding judge, in this case, Judge Carter. She had been in charge for nearly five years and had a reputation of leniency, much to the chagrin of many of her colleagues. A story about her compassionate approach to youth appeared in the local daily newspaper, which outlined her philosophy of redemption rather than punishment. On the basis of that unique philosophy, a program called ArtWorks was born. More about that later.

After a lengthy process, maneuvering through the juvenile justice system, Jamaal learned he could be looking at up to a year of confinement due to his previous history. Entering Judge Carter's courtroom, he remembered where he was to go, even before Officer Kindly pointed to the table where his public defender was sitting patiently. The judge was already there, having presided over a half dozen cases prior to Jamaal's. Jamaal found it hard to believe what he heard next.

"Hello, Jamaal. I'd like to say that it is nice to see you again, but you know that would not be truthful, don't you, Jamaal?" Judge Carter said.

"How could she remember me after the hundreds of other kids who've been here before me?" Jamaal thought to himself. "Okay," he grunted almost under his breath. But she heard him.

"Okay yourself, Jamaal, let's get on with it. You did it again, you robbed a neighbor or at least tried to, before getting caught again. What to do with you?" she nearly shouted. She then delivered his sentence:

"I don't know why I'm going to do what I'm going to do with you, Jamaal, but I see something in you that could be very positive. I can't quite put my finger on it, but I don't think incarceration will help you. I'm going to refer you to a new program called ArtWorks. It's designed to empower kids like you with what they hope will be a positive outcome. It is done through the use of a paintbrush. You, along with kids like you, will be asked to paint murals for the next three months. Now hear this, Jamaal, you will even be paid to do this, in order that you can make restitution to your victims as well as to your legal, financial obligation. Think of it as a summer job. Then, when you've completed this, and you will, I want you to come back here and tell me all about it. Can you do that, Jamaal? We'll see what happens next. Is this 'Okay' with you, Jamaal?"

"Okay," he said, this time a little louder.

"See you in three months. Next case."

Jamaal's new life was about to begin, all this before his sixteenth birthday.

the Beginning, Part I

My name is Mike Peringer and I'm the director of marketing for Process Heating Company. For nearly sixty years we've been located in the heart of an area called SODO, manufacturing heating systems for a variety of industries throughout the world.

SODO originally was short for South of the Dome meaning south of the Kingdome, a major sports stadium, located on the northern boundary of Seattle's primary industrial area. The Kingdome was imploded to make way for a new football stadium a few years later. The term SODO, coined by a major developer in the area, stuck. It now stands for South of Downtown and is about four square miles that contains about two thousand businesses and some fifty thousand employees. It is exclusively industrial with no residential housing except for a smattering of artist workspaces.

During an expansion of our space, I had volunteered to move my office temporarily to a small building next door, one that the company purchased a few years back. Actually it is a small house that was originally the General Electric Home of the Future at the Seattle's World's Fair in 1962. After the fair, a number of buildings at the Seattle Center grounds were offered for sale, cheap, and the-then property owner decided to move it next to our facility. When we purchased it, it stood vacant, and when I moved in, I was the only tenant. That's why I was concerned with the sounds I kept hearing from the space next to mine.

At first I thought it was a large rat. Rats seem to have invaded the industrial area lately. Maybe it was due to the unseasonably warm autumn. Anyway, I have never heard a rat scurry. I was determined to locate the source of that scurrying sound. These rats took on the form of transients who when seeking shelter, situated themselves in the vacant space next to my office. This fact will take on more significance as the story develops. Since we were remodeling part of the building, it was easy for the rats to enter after our plant closed late in the afternoon.

I didn't know how many rats were hunkering down in our space but they must have heard me coming, because all of a sudden, the door flew open as I approached. Six rats ran out and dispersed in the immediate area. As I entered, I detected a specific aroma, one I don't have to describe. What a mess! Later that morning, I, along with some co-workers, cleaned up the space, and more importantly, installed new safeguards in the forms of reinforced doors and locks. If nothing else, new tenants down the road would appreciate this added security.

Later that day, several rats returned, looking for belongings that were now in the nearby garbage dumpster. We could see them urinating on nearby cars, even kicking them on occasion. All we had to do is walk out the door of our offices, and they immediately scattered. This type of event became a regular occurrence. My boss and I decided we had had enough. I called 911 for help. During the course of subsequent meetings with the Crime Prevention folks at the Seattle Police Department (SPD), we learned that this type of situation was rampant throughout our area. When we asked what we could do about it, we were told that we needed to form a community group or association of businesses. As it stood, there was virtually no means of communicating en masse with the several departments at city hall that had civic jurisdiction. We were also informed of a rash of burglaries that had occurred in the area, usually at night after all the workers were gone. Because, historically, criminal activity in the area was very low, police presence was absent, making it a haven for those with a drug habit or other needs.

It was suggested that a community meeting take place with those affected most, local business owners and managers. With the help of the SPD, we located a list of businesses and a room that we thought would be large enough to accommodate area businessmen at an early morning meeting. We ordered pastries and coffee and a meeting was held at 7 A.M. on a Wednesday morning at the old Rainier Brewery Mountain Room.

None of us could believe what happened. More than five hundred people showed up. They crowded into a rather large room (actually a bar with tables – after all, it was a brewery). Some actually had to peer in from outside the door. Needless to say, cars were parked everywhere within a half mile.

At 7:30, the Chief of Police tapped the microphone. Interestingly, that's all it took. The buzz of folks talking ceased, and attention was directed to the front of the hall. Even though most knew who he was (how many police officers have three stars on his or her collar?), he introduced himself. "Good morning, I'm Fred Fitzpatrick, and I work for the Seattle Police Department. I understand there are some public safety problems in the area. We'd like to address them and work with you to find solutions."

It didn't take long before he introduced the two precinct commanders in whose areas SODO was located. Each discussed his responsibilities and perspective. Inasmuch as resources are at a minimum, it was not too practical for SPD patrols to spend much time in the area, but preventive measures and education could be introduced. In other words, we were pretty much on our own. We then heard from the crime prevention folks.

When it was all over, about an hour later, the Chief said, "I have an idea. Mike Peringer is the person who brought this to our attention. He's standing over there." He was pointing at me. I, surprised, raised my hand. "Would you like to see Mike begin some type of association of business owners for the area? That way, you would have a voice in city affairs, a voice that is now missing. Raise your hands if you agree." Virtually every hand, from all five hundred attendees, was raised. Then he said, "Okay then, would you pay dues to belong to such an organization?" This was, of course, the magic question. The hands did not go up quite as fast, but most of them did. "That settles it," he continued. "Mike, they are all yours. I'm sure you will be hearing from him in the next few days."

With that, Seattle's finest, after talking to a few individuals with specific questions, got in their police cars and were gone. As was everyone else. They had all signed in, so I had their places of business, phone numbers, etc.

My boss and I went back to our company only to find a few others already there who had been at the meeting. We invited them to our conference room and thus we formed the SODO Business Association, without which there would not be an ArtWorks.

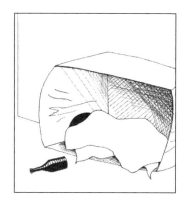

the Beginning, Part II

It had rained the night before our big neighborhood meeting, but was now sunny. It was supposed to warm up to the low 70's by mid-afternoon. We had just finished our morning coffee when Donna asked if I could join her on a tour of the area. I said yes.

Donna was with Seattle Public Utilities and in charge of the city's anti-graffiti program. She also directed the area's cleanups of business communities. Because SODO was clearly the largest, we were successful in getting a $25,000 grant to assist our newly formed Association in cleaning up the area. This was particularly important since there is a direct correlation between criminal activity and lack of cleanliness, particularly graffiti.

We hopped in her official city vehicle and she took me to the E-3 Busway. The Busway is along Fifth Avenue about a block from my office and stretches two miles from the stadium area just south of Pioneer Square to Spokane Street near SODO's southern boundary. It is used exclusively by buses to get sixteen thousand folks in and out of downtown Seattle.

Dedicated solely to buses, the busway should have been off limits to even Donna's official car. But, we were lucky and made it all the way without being cited by transit police.

"Just look at this, Mike!" Donna exclaimed. "Have you ever seen anything like it?"

I hadn't.

Along each side were transients' camps, overgrown weeds, and vines so tall you couldn't see the fence that separated certain buildings from the main street, and items I don't care to mention. She stopped along what was a narrow shoulder and we got out of her car. We walked for a few hundred feet to examine the situation. Not only were there piles of garbage but extensive graffiti on virtually all of the sixty-five buildings situated along the two miles. I have to admit that some of the graffiti was artistic in design and implementation, while most were simply crude words marking the tagger's territory. Simply put, the whole two miles was a disaster. And this was the first thing bus riders saw when they entered the city and the last thing when they left, all sixteen thousand of them! The only saving grace was the sight of the beautiful Seattle skyline visible in the north, on trips into the city.

On re-entering Donna's car, neither of us said anything for a few moments. Then we both said at the same time, "What a mess!" Back to the coffee shop we went.

"I've got an idea, Mike," Donna said. "You have a grant of $25,000. Let's take some of it and hire a grant-writing specialist to help us prepare a program and request for additional funds for some murals. The murals would be put on the back of these buildings, say about a dozen or so, to replace the ugly graffiti. We can use some of the grant money to clean up the busway and paint out the other graffiti. I know a guy."

And, on that warm day in mid-June, 1995, ArtWorks was born.

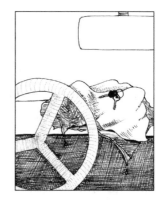

kenny

Wrong place at the wrong time.

That was the story of Kenny's life. He always managed to find himself in trouble for things that happened around him.

Like the time the nerdy kid sitting next to him in Math asked him to pass a note to the girl in front of him. The teacher saw the note being passed, assumed it was from Kenny and made him read it out loud. To his extreme embarrassment, it was a sappy love note, complete with quotes from Shakespeare.

From that moment on, the girl giggled every time she had to pass papers back, and the teacher took to calling Kenny, "The Bard," whatever that meant.

Or the time some senior boys pulled the fire alarm in the locker room while he was in the shower after gym class. Rather than run out naked, Kenny chose to dress first and risk being caught in a fire. When the school principal and custodian came into the locker room, he was putting his shoes on, and suddenly became the prime suspect. It took watching the school's security tapes of the two boys racing out of the locker room, laughing their heads off, to convince the school authorities that Kenny had been an innocent bystander.

But this time was the worst of all. For one thing it involved the police. And the courts. Kenny admitted to his family that technically he had done what he was accused of, that he had taken the car. But he never did manage to explain the circumstances in a way that kept the look of reproach from his brother's eyes. Or the look of deep sadness and disappointment from his mother's.

That spring day when he was first arrested, it had been unusually hot for Seattle, with five-day stretches in the nineties. In the Pacific Northwest, the temperature rarely rises that high until late July or August. A heat wave while school was still in session grated on everyone's nerves. Looking to beat the heat, Kenny and his friends started going to Madison Park to swim, as soon as the last bell rang. It took two buses to get to the beach. Almost as soon as they rushed into the cold waters of Lake Washington, they had to go back to the hot sticky bus stop to make the trek home.

"Man, this blows," Kenny complained to his buddy, Maxter. "The bus sucks."

Maxter nodded. "Not as bad as this bus stop stinks. It smells like pee. Why do bus stops have to smell like pee all the time?"

"I dunno." Kenny looked longingly at the cars as they rushed by. Most of them were empty except for the driver. "If only we could drive! I can't believe we still have to wait two whole years before we can even get our permits. That's just stupid. I know how to drive."

Maxter hooted, "Yeah, right! Only because your brother stole the car all the time to teach you."

Kenny grinned, "And he only taught me because he knew I'd tell Mom he'd been taking it so he and Janie could go make out."

"Too bad he's not around anymore. I bet we could get him to take us to the beach." Maxter dug into his pocket for his bus pass.

"Yeah," Kenny said in a low voice. His brother, Antonio, had moved last year to Alaska to work in a cannery, where the money was amazing, particularly because there was nowhere to spend it. Nenana, where Antonio wound up, boasted fewer than 350 residents. "You should come up here to old "Neena" when you get old enough, Kenny. The money is amazing even though the job is nasty. You slime fish guts out all day into this huge stinking trough twelve hours at a stretch. But then at night, all we do is drink and hit on girls. Everyone thinks I'm a native. I make the chicks try to guess what tribe I'm from. They never believe me when I tell them I'm just black."

Kenny and Antonio had never known their father, while their mother was what she laughingly referred to as "just regular black, which means a whole lot of who knows what." Each boy had long straight hair and deep almond-shaped eyes the color of hazelnuts. More often than not, Kenny was mistaken for Indian, as in from India. Sometimes he would lead people on, adopting the voice of Apoo from The Simpsons, using words like "vindaloo" and asking if there was any curry left over for tea. But soon enough he would crack himself up and let others in on it. "I'm just a good old American mutt," he would say.

Generally, Kenny got good grades, but stuck up in his third floor room with only a weak fan to move the stifling air around, the heat made concentration difficult at best. One night, while trying to remember the differences between Presidents Andrew Jackson and Andrew Johnson he found himself staring out the window toward his mother's ancient Dodge Dart. A sickly yellow color, the car had been old when she bought it, burned oil in a thick cloud spewing behind the car as it coughed down the street, and smelled vaguely of sweaty feet, but it ran.

If only he could borrow it for an hour! Just long enough to drive over to the beach, dive in, cool off and drive home. It wouldn't even take an hour. Half-hour, tops.

No one would miss him, or the car. Kenny pictured himself running down the slight hill from the parking lot, the stiff browned grass poking his bare feet, until he reached the smooth sand and, at last, the brief shock of the cold water. Lake Washington was notorious for not really warming up until mid-July, but when the city heated up like it had the past week. Kenny didn't care if there were ice floes.

"I'm going over to Larla's." His mother poked her head into the room, startling Kenny out of his reverie. "She got one of those new portable ACs. You wanna come?"

Larla was his mother's best friend. Kenny liked her, but knew if he went, Larla's eleven-year-old daughter Lori would pester him the whole time. Lori thought that since their mothers were best friends, they should be, too, except they had nothing in common. Lori was into manga-style Japanese animation to a degree that Kenny thought bordered on obsession. She spent all her money on manga comics, DVDs or conventions. And she had this strange idea that if she could just explain it to Kenny the right way, Kenny would suddenly love it, too. Only Kenny thought manga was dumb. Sure, the artistic style was cool, but not cool enough to devote one's whole life and attention to it.

So Kenny replied to his mother, "Nah, I gotta study. I have my American History final this week."

Once he heard her slam the front door, Kenny tried to return to his book but after a few minutes, the daydream of the beach reclaimed him. He looked longingly at the car out front. If Larla's new air conditioner was even half as good as promised, his mom would be gone for hours, if not all night. The two women would finish off a bottle or two of cheap wine or sherry and get all weepy over the various men who did them wrong. She would be sure to call and blearily let him know when she decided to spend the night, but not for at least two hours. Kenny looked at the car again. It wasn't as if he was going to go joy riding. A quick dip in the lake. Easy in, easy out. No sweat. Literally, Kenny thought.

Quickly, he found a towel from the cupboard and ran downstairs. In the unlikely event that his mom did come home before midnight, he wrote a note, "Be back soon," and left it on the kitchen table. Outside, Kenny reached into the wheel well of the car to find the Hide-A-Key where his mother always kept the spare key. With a last look around, he started the car, wincing at the harsh screech. His heart was pounding and he could feel sweat pouring in little rivulets down the middle of his back. To reach the pedals he had to sit up so straight his body didn't touch the seat. He chose not to move the seat up in case he forgot to put it back when he returned the car.

Traffic was light and it seemed like only minutes before he was angling the car into a parking space. Carefully checking to see no one was watching, he returned the key to its hiding place so he wouldn't have to worry about it falling out of his pocket while he was in the water. Then, just as in his dream, he ran down the hill and right into the cold, clear water. Later in the year, after hordes of children swam there day after day, the water would turn an eerie green with churned up algae and the local seaweed. But now it was so clear Kenny could see all the way to the bottom: small rocks and multicolored pebbles mixing with the clouds of sand. For the first time in days, Kenny felt goose bumps rise on his flesh. When his shivers grew too severe and his hands grew wrinkled, he got out of the water.

By the time he reached the car again, he was no longer shivering. Kenny smiled as he started the car. The few minutes of being cooled off was worth it. Now he would be able to get some real studying done.

Gently he pointed the car toward home, but when he pulled away from the curb he was surprised to see his way blocked by a white car. A white car with lights attached to the top.

Oh great, the cops!

Kenny tried to sit up straighter in the seat and cheerfully waved to the car to indicate they could go ahead. Maybe if he acted like there was nothing wrong, they would just drive off and leave him alone. The key was not to panic. If he freaked out, he would be busted for sure.

Unfortunately, it didn't seem to be working. Rather than move their car, one of the police officers got out and started walking toward Kenny. Since the window was already down, Kenny smiled again and tried to be cheerful, "Hot enough for you?"

The officer looked at Kenny. "I need to see your driver's license and proof of insurance, please."

Kenny, still trying to contain his rising panic, reached over the seat to the glove box. It was crammed with papers, old napkins and poorly folded maps. There was even a small bottle of hand lotion and a nine-volt battery in there, but Kenny knew he could look for days and never find a driver's license. He did find a tattered card with the same logo as his mother's insurance company on it, which he handed to the police officer. The officer looked it over before saying, "This is expired. Now, about that driver's license. And why don't I take a look at your car registration while I'm at it?"

Kenny was nearly frantic. He shoved all the non-paper items onto the floor of the car and hastily riffled through the remaining papers. In an old envelope with his mother's handwriting scrawled on it, he found the car registration. "Here you go. I know I put my license in here while I was swimming. It's so hot today, don't you think?"

The officer read the registration and glanced at Kenny. He said, "You keep looking for that license while I run this through the computer. You do know it's illegal to operate a car without proof of proper insurance, right?"

Kenny laughed nervously, "Oh yeah, I know. See, I always forget to take the old insurance cards out of the glove box. I just toss the new one in, so I'm sure it's in here someplace."

The officer nodded, "You keep looking. I'll be right back."

While the man walked back to his car, Kenny tried to control himself. He didn't know what the penalty was for driving without a license, but he was sure it wasn't to let the person drive home. How was he going to get his mother's car home before she did? If he had to take the bus home, he would then have to take it back and hope he didn't get stopped again for anything while he drove back. That would take hours. Well, maybe his mother and Larla were already drunk enough that she wouldn't come home tonight at all. That would give him plenty of time to return the car without her knowing it had been gone.

The police officer returned to Kenny. "Please step out of the car."

Kenny was shocked, "What?" he asked.

The officer stood a few feet from the car, "Please step out of the car, and keep your hands where I can see them."

Puzzled, Kenny did as he was asked. "I don't get it. What's the deal?"

The officer asked him, "Do you have anything on your person that could be used as a weapon?"

Kenny looked down at his shorts, still dripping onto the hot pavement, "No."

"Do you have any identification on your person?"

Oh, thought Kenny, he still wants my driver's license. Great, I'm going to get a ticket for driving without a license. What a pain! "No, I guess I lost it after all. Sorry," he added.

"What's your name?" the officer took out a notebook and a small pen.

"Kenny."

"And do you live on 26th?"

Kenny frowned still puzzled, "Yeah, how did you know where I lived?"

"It's on the car registration you gave me. The one that says this car is registered to a Dorene Turner."

Kenny smiled, "That's my mom. It's her car."

The officer looked at his notebook again. "Uhuh, and does she know you have her car?"

Kenny swallowed, "Well, not exactly. At least not to go swimming. See," he smiled as his mind raced to make up a plausible lie, "she lets me borrow the car all the time to run errands. You know, go to the store for milk or whatever. But she was at her friend's house and when I called to ask her if I could come down here to cool off, the phone was busy. I think--"

The officer cut him off, "Well, it appears that your mother called in this car as stolen less than an hour ago."

Kenny gasped, "Stolen! No, it's not stolen. I just kind of borrowed it."

The officer looked at him. Kenny continued, "No, really! I was only going to go swimming and then I was gonna give it right back."

"Your mom seems to have a different opinion. She reported the vehicle as stolen, and here it is. So I have no choice but to bring you in and impound the vehicle."

"No, you can't do that. See, once Mom finds out it's me who took the car, she'll realize it wasn't stolen. Only borrowed." Kenny's voice was low as he recognized how lame that sounded.

"Well, that may be, but until I hear otherwise, this car is considered stolen, and since you just admitted to taking it, that means I have to take you in. Come on. Is there anything in the car you want to bring with you?"

Kenny looked back at the car replying, "No. I just wanted to go swimming."

At the police station, Kenny was given an orange jumpsuit to wear over his damp shorts and a plastic bag with a comb, toothbrush and small tube of toothpaste. He combed out his hair while he waited in a large empty room. He never felt so alone in his life. Though he had given the officer Larla's phone number, ironically it was indeed busy when the officer tried to call. "Probably Lori talking online to her geek manga friends." After waiting an hour, he was moved to another room, this one with a couch, a table with four chairs and a bookcase filled with tired books, some with the covers half torn off. Kenny settled in with an old copy of *Time* magazine on the couch but the words kept blurring in front of him as he tried to think of how to get out of this mess.

Two hours later, the police officer came back. "Come on, time for your meeting with the detention folks."

"Detention?" Kenny said in surprise, "I thought you were gonna call my mom."

The man looked sad, "I did, Kenny."

"But I didn't steal her car. I borrowed it," he protested loudly.

"I guess your mom didn't see it that way."

"So what happens now?" Kenny asked.

"You go see the judge, tell her what happened and she decides where to go from there."

"Don't I get a lawyer or something?" Kenny's only experience with the law to this point was endless reruns of "Law and Order" on TV.

The officer smiled. "You'll have an advocate there to help you."

In the small courtroom, Kenny met Alice, a short woman with blonde hair. She told him she was there to make sure his interests were represented. Quickly, she asked Kenny a series of questions about how he came to be found driving his mother's car. Kenny told her the whole story truthfully.

"Now, Kenny," Alice said gently, "you do know it's wrong to take other people's possessions without their permission?"

Kenny managed a weak smile, "Yes, I know."

"And you do know that it's illegal to drive without a license?" she continued.

"Yes, I know."

"And that you have to be sixteen to get a license?"

"Yeah." Kenny's voice was soft.

"And that it's illegal to drive without proof of insurance in the car, which you weren't supposed to be driving in the first place?" Alice grinned at Kenny. For the first time in hours, he felt like someone might believe his side of how things had turned out.

"Well, no. That part I didn't know."

"Okay then. Let's go explain what happened." Alice returned a stack of papers into a manila envelope.

Standing in front of the judge, an imposing older woman with grey hair and wire-rimmed glasses, Kenny told what had happened. She listened without comment until he finished. Without looking up from papers on her desk, she asked, "That all?"

"Yes, Your Honor," Alice answered.

"Anyone talk to the mother?"

"Yes, Your Honor, I did." Another woman on the other side of Alice spoke up. Alice whispered to Kenny, "Mrs. Hicks is the prosecutor for the county."

Mrs. Hicks checked her notes. "Ms. Turner did not want to change her report that the car had been stolen."

The judge looked up at this, "Really? And did you explain the circumstances under which her son was found with the car?"

"Yes, I did. It did not change her mind."

"Indeed." The judge did not seem pleased at this. "Anything else?"

Alice pursed her lips, "In light of this, I would like to recommend, given that this is Kenny's first offense and the non-violent nature of his actions, that he be referred to the ArtWorks program, which I believe is slated to start the second week of June. Kenny will be out of school by then."

The judge looked at Kenny. "Kenny are you familiar with ArtWorks?"

"No, I'm not."

"Well, rather than send you to a juvenile facility or give you regular community service for taking the car, you will be assigned to do community service with a youth organization that creates public ArtWorks around the city, mostly by painting those big plywood fences that go around construction sites and on murals on buildings."

Kenny grinned, "Cool! That's my punishment?"

The judge's face grew serious, "No, not cool. This is a serious program with very strict guidelines and requirements. For example, you must be there every day for six hours a day, five days a week. On time, ready to work. They will provide instruction and materials. You will provide your attention. Is this something you would prefer to standard community service?"

Kenny didn't have to think twice. "Yeah, I would definitely prefer it."

"All right, then," the judge said. "Kenny, you are hereby sentenced to complete twenty-four hours of community service within the ArtWorks program."

ArtWorks was housed in a large warehouse south of downtown Seattle. Kenny took the bus early the Monday after school was out for the year. All he knew about the program was what Alice had told him after his meeting with the judge. He would need to be there every day from nine in the morning until four in the afternoon with an hour off for lunch, which he would need to bring. Inside the warehouse he met with Marcus, who would be his mentor. Marcus explained that he was an art student from the University of Washington working with ArtWorks for the summer. Marcus introduced him to a small group of kids standing around, waiting to start. As they went around the semi-circle, Kenny realized that most of them were also referrals from the court system.

"Okay, let's get started." Marcus got their attention. "Now, how many of you have ever painted before?"

A boy standing next to Kenny raised his hand, saying, "You mean, like art? Or like houses?"

The group laughed, and Kenny was relieved to see that Marcus laughed along with them. He had been afraid that the group leaders or mentors would be hard-nosed about everything, but Marcus seemed cool.

"No, I mean either. Art, houses, chairs, whatever." Marcus looked pleased when a few kids raised their hands. "Great, then you can help the others." He led them to the supply area and to the painting dock where the actual painting would take place. "But first, we have to decide on a design. What do you want the panels to look like? Your group is assigned to paint panels for the new building going up downtown near the new symphony hall. Lots of people work in that area, and we want to make sure they have something pretty to look at, not just boring old plywood."

Kenny raised his hand, "Wait a sec, Marcus. You mean we get to decide? You don't just tell us?"

Marcus smiled, "First, you guys don't need to raise your hands to talk. Just remember to be respectful if someone else is talking. But yeah, you design the panels. I'm here to help make sure you stay on the right track and keep it reasonably applicable to the location. Like if we were putting your panels out by the zoo, we wouldn't want a bunch of ships and lake scenes. We'd want animals and jungles and savannahs, right?"

"Since we're going to be by the new hall, should we do musical instruments?" a girl asked.

"Well, not necessarily. Sure that would be cool, but why not some musical notes, too? Or a singer?"

Kenny said, "How 'bout that fat lady with the Viking horns that's supposed to sing at operas?" Everyone laughed, including Marcus.

"Now we're talking. Let's write some of this down."

About halfway through his community service hours, Kenny was called into Marcus's office. The tiny space was cluttered with drawings, photographs of works in progress, pens, pencils and pastel crayons littered the desk. Marcus smiled sheepishly as he cleared a pile of papers from a chair. "Have a seat, Kenny. How's it going?"

Kenny wasn't sure what Marcus meant. Was he simply being friendly or was he really asking?

"Fine, I guess," he replied.

"Good. Glad to hear it. You're getting along with the other guys on your crew okay?"

Kenny started to worry. Was he in trouble? He didn't think he had done anything to get anyone upset with him. He showed up on time every day, worked hard, made sure his workspace was clean before he left. Everyone on the crew got along fine. There were even some kids he started to spend his lunch time with regularly.

"I guess it's fine." Kenny couldn't take it. "Why? Is there something wrong?"

"No, not at all." Marcus was quick to reassure him. "Actually just the opposite. I've been watching you and you really seem to be taking to the program. You're cooperative, helpful, a hard worker, just the kind of kid we want working with us."

"Working with you?" Kenny asked, not sure where this was going.

"Kenny, I was talking to the Executive Director about you, and she'd like to meet with you. We have a proposal for you."

"What kind of proposal?" Kenny looked at Marcus.

"Why don't I let her explain it to you? She's in her office right now." Marcus stood and led the way down the hall to another equally cramped, though decidedly more tidy office. A middle-aged blonde woman was on the phone but waved them in toward two chairs. While she quickly finished her call, Kenny had a chance to look around the office. On the walls were photographs of the director standing in front of various ArtWorks projects around the city. On her desk were framed photos of a family, presumably hers, complete with family dog.

"Sorry that took so long. Kenny, I'm Virginia Stockton. Marcus has been telling me all about you."

Kenny smiled at her. "Nice to meet you, ma'am."

She smiled back, "Please call me Virginia. Most everyone does. Now then, I read over your file this morning. Too bad about the car." She looked at him expectantly.

Kenny's smile faded. "Yeah, well it was dumb to take the car like I did. I should have just turned the hose on over my head."

Virginia nodded. "Yes, that would have been a better choice. Life is all about choices, Kenny. I'm sorry you had to learn that at such a young age. But--" she brightened, "now I have another choice for you that shouldn't be quite so dramatic. How would you like to come work for us?"

"Work for you?" he glanced over at Marcus. "But I can't. I still have six weeks of community service to do. And our panels aren't ready yet. I can't bail on the team."

Marcus replied, "You wouldn't be bailing on the team, Kenny. You'd be helping another team get started. You see, we have another crew that's supposed to start next Monday and run through the rest of summer. We want you to work with me as a sort of junior mentor. You and I would help them design their panels and get them started on prepping and painting them. Their job site is much smaller than the one you've been working on so it won't take quite as long to be up and running."

"But what about my crew? I mean, the one I'm on now?" Kenny asked.

"That's what I meant about life being full of choices," she explained. "Right now your crew is at the point where they can make it, if one or two of you move to other projects. But this new crew would really benefit from having someone who's been through the program. Marcus, as great as he is, doesn't have the same experience that you do."

"So I wouldn't so much be a part of the crew, as a leader?" Kenny asked.

Marcus grinned. "Well, I wouldn't go quite that far. I would still be in charge, but you would be doing more of the actual hands-on work with the new crew since I'll have more than just your original group to work with now. You would be the new group's 'Go To' guy when they have questions about how we do stuff around here. What do you say?"

Both Marcus and Virginia looked at Kenny expectantly. Kenny thought about it a moment. "Sure." He laughed at the idea. "I can be a junior mentor. But if I do okay, does that mean maybe next summer I might be a real mentor?"

Virginia replied, "I don't see why not. But let's cross that bridge when we come to it."

The rest of the summer went by in a blur. Kenny arrived at the warehouse every morning as before, only now he got there at eight in order to give himself time to set up his crew's workspace for the day, double-check that the previous day's paperwork was filled out properly and any number of other details that his new position required. He still took the bus to work, but now when he rode he noticed with pride other ArtWorks sites around the city, eagerly pointing them out to other passengers. He looked forward to heading down Fifth Avenue where huge, colorful murals now covered what used to be dull beige or grey buildings.

Then, on the last day of the summer program, Kenny felt a tinge of sadness. He had completed his required service hours about a week before, but asked Virginia if he could stay on to finish out the year with his crew. She readily agreed. "And remember, Kenny, next summer if you want to come work for us again, give me a call. We'd be glad to have you back with us. And this time," she added with a twinkle in her eye, "we'll pay you for your time."

"I sure will, Virginia. Thanks. For everything, I mean." Kenny smiled at her. At first he had been intimidated by the small woman who ran such a big, busy program, but as the weeks went by, he had begun to see her as more of a colleague, if not a friend. He would still eat his lunch with his old crew, but whenever he saw her crossing the parking lot or inside the warehouse, she gave him a bright smile and a cheerful wave. For the first time, it seemed like someone liked him and respected him solely based on his work performance.

Virginia told him as she handed him her business card, "Kenny, I wrote my home number on the back. If ever you need to get in touch with me, don't hesitate. I don't think you'll get into the kind of trouble that brought you to us in the first place, but life can be tricky sometimes. Even if you just want to talk, I'm here."

Kenny shook her hand. "I understand, Virginia. That means a lot to me. Thanks."

Six months later, Kenny and Maxter slumped on the couch in Kenny's living room, video game consoles in their hands. Kenny's was on its last legs but he was determined to wring every minute of entertainment he could out of it before it gave out completely. Suddenly the doorbell rang. Since he was already losing, Kenny gladly set aside his controller to answer it. Three guys from the neighborhood, Bobby, Jonas and Travis, pushed past Kenny into the house. They had all known each other since they were babies, but Kenny was never sure if they hung out together because they were friends or just because they lived in close proximity.

"Hey, dude, got any food?" Bobby was notorious for cleaning out other people's fridges. Kenny's mother more than once had lectured him on the price of groceries, demanding that he stand up to the larger boy to put an end to his food raids. To date, Kenny had been unsuccessful.

"No, man, my mom hasn't been shopping this week. Sorry," Kenny said lamely. As if to prove him a liar, Bobby stomped his way into the kitchen, opening cupboards and drawers. But Kenny had been telling the truth. Other than a few packets of ramen noodles and some diet soup, there was nothing. Kenny's mother was rarely home these days and she relied on Kenny to find his own meals most of the time.

"Dude, that is weak," Bobby protested. He glared at Kenny as if this would make the smaller boy suddenly reveal a secret closet filled with junk food. "Let's go to the mini-mart. You know, five-fingered discount. All-you-can-take-buffet."

Kenny winced. "No way, guys. If you want to go shoplifting, leave me out of it."

Travis punched Kenny in the arm. "Don't be such a baby, Kenny. Geez, we have money. Bobby's only kidding." To prove it, Travis held out his wallet, fat with bills.

"Yeah, man, you take everything so seriously these days. What did that juvie program do to you?"

Kenny refused to be baited. He knew the skills he learned over the summer had taught him more than just how to prep plywood for painting.

"C'mon, you guys. Bobby's got his license finally. Let's go find something to do other than sit around listening to his stomach growl." Jonas was one of those kids who was unable to sit still. Constantly in motion, he paced the hallway from the living room to the kitchen. He reminded Kenny of a squirrel.

As the boys left the kitchen, Kenny hesitated. Maxter glanced at him. "Kenny, you coming?"

In the back of his mind, Kenny searched for a reason not to go. Sure, other than Maxter, these boys were not who he would generally want to spend time with, but his homework was done, his video game system was tapped out, no idea when or if his mom would be back today. Why not?

Once outside, he saw the other boys had already taken all the "good spots" in the car; shotgun, window seats. He climbed over Travis's legs to sit in the center seat, thankful Jonas with his restless legs and arms had won the coveted front seat. On the way to the store, the boys blasted the radio, singing loudly and wildly off key to any song they remotely knew. Bobby, surprisingly, was a good driver, making sure to use his turn signals, stay in his own lane, and yield the right of way when necessary.

When he pulled into the store parking lot, he turned to face the other boys. "Okay, dudes, now whatever you do, don't get caught. In, out, nobody gets hurt." When he saw the panic on Kenny's face, he guffawed. "God, Kenny! You're so easy. I'm just kidding."

Nevertheless, to be on the safe side, Kenny decided to stay in the car. He was relieved to see through the big plate window that all the boys paid cash for their snacks. As the car slowly worked its way out of the lot, Maxter threw Kenny a pack of mini-donuts. "For the road," he explained.

Suddenly Bobby swore loudly and proficiently. Kenny looked out the window to see flashing lights next to the car. Travis said, "Pull over to the side so they can get by, Bobby. You always have to give the right away to cops," he added smugly. "Only another two weeks and I'm out of Driver's Ed." Bobby, however, felt anything but smug. He tried to pull the car over to the curb but there were too many parked cars in the way. He swore again. Kenny watched as the police car slowed behind them. A loud voice came from the blue and white car's PA system. "Pull the car over immediately."

Bobby appeared to be thinking this over first. Jonas told him, "Dude, you gotta pull over."

"What? So I can get arrested like little Kenny did last summer? I don't think so."

Kenny listened in disbelief. "What do you mean?" he asked, afraid to know the answer.

"Duh, it's not my car." Bobby was swearing again, but realizing he had no alternative, pulled the car over in the first available space. The police cruiser pulled up beside them, effectively blocking them from getting out. Just like last summer, Kenny realized, with a growing sense of fear.

After rolling down his window, Bobby sat perfectly still as the officer approached "Hey, how ya doing?" he asked trying to sound personable.

"Is this your car?" the officer asked firmly.

"Sort of," Bobby said lamely.

"Sort of. What does that mean exactly?"

"It's my neighbor's car," Bobby explained. "But he lets me borrow it."

"Did your neighbor know you borrowed it tonight?"

"Well, kinda. Sort of," Bobby stammered.

"License." The officer held out his hand as Bobby gave him his new driver's license.

"This your current address?" he asked.

"Yeah," whispered Bobby

"And how long have you lived there?"

"All my life," Bobby replied, quickly adding, "Sir."

The officer stared at Bobby. "So if you've lived on Twenty-Fifth all your life, how come the owner of this car, who reported it stolen two hours ago, lives over in North Ridge, all the way on the other side of town?"

Bobby raised his eyebrows, trying to think of a reasonable explanation. Finally, he admitted, "I dunno."

The officer stepped back from the window. "All right, everyone out of the car. Keep your hands where I can see them." He clicked a button on the radio attached to his collar. Kenny heard something about needing another unit at their location. When the officer whose name badge read Banks lined them up on the curb, Kenny asked him, "Why do we have to stay? I didn't know the car was stolen."

Banks pointed to the curb, "Park it, kid. I'll get to you in a minute." He went down the line writing down each boy's name, address, phone number and parents' names. Then he walked back to the car and entered the information into his computer. After taking a few notes, he returned, stopping in front of Kenny.

"So, Kenny. This isn't your first time stealing a car, eh?"

"I didn't steal it!" Kenny protested. "I didn't even know it was stolen."

"Sure," said Banks, though he clearly didn't believe it. "Just like last time when it wasn't your fault either."

"No, that was my fault. But I did my community service." Kenny told him.

"Glad to hear it. Now stand up and turn around."

Kenny and the other boys turned around. Banks, with the help of the second officer who showed up a minute later, attached plastic handcuffs to their wrists. Kenny and Maxter were placed in Banks' car.

"Kenny, what's going to happen to us?" Maxter whispered.

"For now, we go to the police station. After we tell them what happened, they're sure to let us go." Overhearing this, Banks snorted, "Yeah, right. You wish."

Kenny and Maxter were silent all through the ride to the station. Banks typed out their statements about what had happened that evening, before leaving them in the same large room Kenny remembered from his last arrest. He had hoped to never see it again. After waiting nearly two hours, Banks returned.

"Okay, guys, who wants to make the first phone call home?" he asked altogether too cheerfully.

Kenny raised his hand. "Mr. Banks, do we have to call our parents? I mean, can I call a guardian-type person instead?"

Banks considered this. "It says in your file you don't have one, but if you want to waste your call, that's your choice." He pointed to a wall phone. "No long distance, obviously."

Kenny pulled out his wallet, thankful his belongings hadn't been checked in yet. He found the card Virginia gave him last August. Hoping against hope that she would be there, he dialed the handwritten number on the back. On the fourth ring, a man picked up.

"Hello, may I speak to Virginia please?"

The man sounded surprised, "Yes, who's this?"

Kenny glanced over at Maxter and Banks. Neither appeared to be listening. "It's Kenny Turner. I worked with Virginia last summer. At Panels for Progress," he prompted.

"Kenny Turner?" The man sounded even more surprised. "Virginia mentioned you. Hold on."

After what seemed like an eternity, Kenny heard Virginia on the line. "Kenny? What is it? Are you hurt?"

Kenny suddenly felt like he was going to cry. Relief swept through him, "No, I'm not hurt, Virginia. But I need your help."

"What happened? Where are you?" Virginia's voice was filled with concern.

"I'm at the police station."

"The police station! Kenny what did you do?"

"Nothing. I swear it. There were these guys I know and we went to the store but I stayed in the car, and then as we were leaving the cops pulled us over, and the car was stolen, but I didn't know it was stolen." Kenny felt the tear streaming down his face as the words poured out.

"Oh, Kenny." Virginia sounded sad and disappointed.

He tried to convince her. "Honestly, Virginia, I didn't know. I swear it."

He heard Virginia sigh. "Look, I'll be right there. Is there an officer I can talk to?"

Kenny handed the phone over to Banks who motioned for him to sit down again with Maxter.

"Was your mom mad?" Maxter asked anxiously.

"I didn't call her."

"Why not?"

"I just didn't, okay?" he snapped at his friend.

Soon it was Maxter's turn. When he finished, Banks took them through the booking process and returned them to the waiting room. After waiting another two hours, he brought them to the same small courtroom as Kenny had been to last year. He saw Virginia waiting for him near the front. Alice was also there. She smiled when she saw Kenny, but he could see it was a smile laced with sadness.

Kenny realized behind the desk at the front was the same judge he had last year. He hoped this was a good sign that someone would believe him.

"Kenny, is what you told Officer Banks in your statement true?" the judge asked.

"I swear it. I had no idea Bobby took that car. Stupid Bobby, I don't even know why I hang out with him," Kenny grumbled.

"Well, you won't be hanging with anyone for a while, Kenny. This is a serious breach of your deferment agreement."

"Deferment? I thought I did my sentence when I finished the ArtWorks thing?

The judge peered at him over her glasses. "Kenny, that was just part of your sentence. The other part was that you would stay out of trouble for a period of three years or your full sentence would be re-established."

"But I thought that was just if I got in trouble again." Kenny couldn't believe this was happening to him.

"And what do you call this?"

"But it wasn't my fault! If I had known, I never would have gotten into the car with those guys."

"Be that as it may, you did get into the car, you were found in a stolen vehicle, and so your initial sentence is being reinstated."

"So I'm going to jail?"

"Yes, you are. But not tonight. Tomorrow morning is soon enough. Is your mother here to pick you up?"

At this, Virginia stood up. "Excuse me, your Honor. Kenny's mother is unavailable. If it is all right with you, I will take Kenny home with me. You can be assured that he will be back here bright and early."

"Kenny, is there some reason your mother is not here to pick you up?" the judge asked.

"She won't pick me up." he replied. "She told me if I got in trouble again not to call her. That's why I called Virginia."

The judge shook her head slightly. "All right, then, I award temporary custody of Kenny Turner to Virginia Stockton until such time as she relinquishes him to the juvenile detention facility tomorrow morning. Be here at nine o'clock." With a flurry of paperwork, she left the room.

Virginia stood next to Kenny. "You're sure there's no point in calling your mom? Maybe if she understood the circumstances she would…"

Kenny cut her off, "No, she wouldn't. She told me last time to never call her from the police station again. As far as she's concerned if I'm old enough to get into trouble, I'm old enough to get out of it. That's why my brother left. The last time he got busted, she kicked him out."

Virginia nodded slowly. "Back to my house then. I have some of my son's clothes that I haven't gotten rid of yet, if you want to change into something fresh tomorrow."

"Then back into the pretty orange jumpsuit. Can't wait." Kenny smiled at her with melancholy eyes. They turned and headed for home. If only for a night.

ArtWorks,
the Early Years

His name was Ron Sorenson. As it turns out, I already was familiar with his expertise as a planner, grant writer, computer whiz and with other attributes that set him apart from many municipal-oriented specialists. Ron had been hired as a consultant to the consultants who worked with us on our neighborhood plan. The mayor had decided that each community would develop a plan as part of a citywide document for the future. Because our area, made up exclusively of businesses, was unique, the government asked us to hire consultants to assist us. Actually, that was a good idea, inasmuch as none of us in the SODO Business Association had either the skill or time to accomplish such a task. So, Ron was hired. He was already working with other community groups in a similar capacity.

Donna and I met with him, again over coffee, to outline our approach to city funding for up to a dozen murals, along what Ron would quickly name the Urban Art Corridor. We surely would have struggled with a name if we decided it was necessary. His suggestion had a ring that was very positive. We were certain it would be well received by potential funders. Later on, we formally requested the name of the E-3 Busway be changed to Urban Art Corridor.

The second major task was to request a grant from the Department of Neighborhoods' Neighborhood Matching Grant Program, a two-part process. First is a "small and simple" grant that gives community groups a modest amount for funding projects, such as signs, marketing programs, outreach, i.e., small programs. The funds can also be used to develop larger grant requests. That is where ArtWorks' mural program fit in. Ron created a request for $10,000 to be locally matched by businesses providing in-kind assistance, which would lead to a major grant request for the dozen murals on the Art Corridor.

Since Ron had done it a number of times, he knew how to do it in a matter of hours, not days. We were requesting an amount necessary to produce twelve murals on twelve buildings along the two-mile busway. This included funding for the time involved in set-up, talking to building owners and artists to create and supervise such a project, as many as twelve lead artists or muralists. Then there was the big question: Who would actually produce the murals? Ron included all of this in the final funding request. When all was said and done, we asked for $80,000 from the City to be matched with another $80,000 as described earlier, for a total of $160,000. Wow!

Part of Ron's request included the hiring of an overall mural supervisor, later called our Executive Director. Even before we got word that our request had been accepted (not granted, mind you), we started the task of finding a suitable leader who would handle day-to-day operations. We were breaking new ground here. There was not a similar program anywhere in the area. So, at times, we were exploring in the dark.

While we were working day to day on our next steps, the City's decision makers were reviewing our proposal. The fact that they had awarded us the smaller amount worked in our favor, but it was not assured that we would get the larger amount. In that process, we had to appear and make our pitch to the committee that would decide.

Ron and I made our way to City Hall one evening, knowing we were breaking new ground. Armed with drawings, photographs and ten written proposals accompanying a slide show depicting the actual locations of the murals, mural images, budgets, and other supporting documents, we made our pitch to convince the committee that the program was worthwhile to the community and the city.

We knew as soon as we entered the conference room that we were in for a long night.

More than one committee member made a remark about a program that seemed so totally new and unique they found it hard to fathom its benefits to the city. They didn't once mention the benefits to the young people who would make up the program or the resulting public art projects. Fortunately, I knew one of the members and attempted to break the ice with some small talk before we began our pitch. Then we were on.

Ron is an excellent presenter; thus he did most of the talking. I spent most of my time describing our Association and its relationship to the concept and the program

An hour later, after we answered a few questions, we left the room wondering how we did. We would find out within two weeks.

Billy

"OOOO, BILLLLLLLLLY, IT'S TIME TO GET UP!" my sister yelled at me.

"Ahhhhhhhhhhhh," I moaned out loud; "is it time to get up already?" My clock flashed 9:30 A.M. I got dressed in a hurry and raced down the stairs. I was going to be late, again. Before racing out the door, I quickly grabbed a piece of toast my mom had set out for me, and my work bag. Sprinting as fast as I could, I prayed that the bus would arrive late today.

The bus stop came into view and my worst fear had come true. The bus had been on time. I was now going to be very late. Because the next bus wouldn't come for another hour, I began the long walk to work. Walking to work always made me think about a lot of things.

"My alarm didn't go off, and I missed the bus. I walked four miles to get here. That's why I'm late," I said to Joe Blomish, my boss.

"I'm sorry, Billy, but this has happened too many times. You're late every other day. Even though you're one of my best workers and know a great deal about computers, I am still going to have to let you go," Joe said in a very polite but firm voice.

"But, Mr. Blomish, you don't understand! I need this job. If I lose it, then my family can't make the rent. My dad will have to get another job," I said, pleading for him to change his mind.

"I am so sorry, Billy, but I can't have you coming in late all the time. It doesn't look good for the other employees," he said with a rougher tone.

I felt tears spring to my eyes in frustration and anger.

"Well, I guess tomorrow can be your last day," he said.

"Fine!" I yelled as he disappeared around the corner.

Even though every bone in my body ached because of the long walk, I still worked hard. I tried to numb my whole body. My father always told me that "pain is good; it tells us our bodies are working, and it helps us be strong." I never got that. Unlike my father, I don't like pain; it always makes me feel weak, not strong. Like, I am so weak that my body has a hard time surviving.

Mr. Blomish owned a small but important computer company. I worked there on Saturdays and Sundays until it was so dark outside that you couldn't even see your own hand waving right in front of your face.

I guess Mr. Blomish was right. I was one of his hardest workers. I could cut twice as many wires as the other guys. And I never took breaks. Almost all the guys smoked and took breaks constantly. I was kind of an outcast. None of the other guys talked to me and I was too afraid to talk to them.

How was I going to tell my mom that I lost this job? We counted on the money so much. And Dad, this could put him over the top and he'd start drinking again. Why hadn't my alarm gone off? How could I have missed the bus again? What was I going to do?

I slowly walked to the assembly line with my head down. I could feel the other guys staring at me. I looked up and growled, "What you lookin' at?" They quickly went back to work. My job was to cut the wires for the external hard-drive plugs. I was the end man, so my work all went into a bin for the next line to connect the wires. I had hoped to get promoted there. The money was twice as much. I knew how to connect the wires. I liked to fiddle around with them. I spent most of my lunch hour figuring out how the entire motherboard went together.

Man, did I blow it! I would never be able to find a job that paid this good for weekend work. "At least I won't have to tell my parents that I lost my job until tomorrow," I thought to myself. "If maybe if I work extra hard, he won't fire me."

Beep! "Will all workers please turn off their machines and report to the mess hall? That is all." Beep, the intercom buzzed. Stepping off to the side, I had no desire to go to the mess hall and watch all the other guys. As usual, I went straight to the bathroom to hide. Usually I was alone, but as soon as I locked my stall door, I heard the swish of the outside door opening. I instinctively put my feet up on the stall door, so nobody would know I was there. "Who would come into the bathroom during lunch time?" I asked myself. I later found out who it was, and my life changed forever.

"I told you, boss, this is the perfect place," one dude said.

"Shut it, Larry, I'm trying to think here. Hmmmmm, I don't know. Joey, what do you think of this place?"

"Well, boss, I agree with Larry, I think this place is perfect. I mean, come on, there are no security cameras anywhere!"

"Yeah, I guess it's okay. Then this will do. Boys, we are going to be rich! Come on, let's celebrate!"

Then it hit me. I was going to sneeze. I couldn't help it. "AHHHCHOOO!"

"Hey boss, I think someone's in that stall!" There was nothing I could do. I was trapped. Even though the door was locked, they managed to force it open. I was face to face with the men that I assumed were going to rob the place. "Guys, please, I don't think you want to kill me, I mean I'm not worth it and I won't tell I…" But the boss cut me off with a wicked smile and said "We're not going to kill you, you're going to help us."

"Oh, okay," I said in a timid shaky voice.

A large hand grabbed the front of my shirt and pulled me out of the stall and shoved me against the wall. "Does anyone know you're in here?" he snarled.

"No, I come in here to be alone at lunch all the time," I whispered. He still had his huge hands wrapped around my shirt. The buttons were ready to pop off.

"Let him down, Joey. I think this is going to work out nicely," said the man I came to know as Larry, the Boss.

There was a commotion outside, and Larry looked up in a panic. "Now's not the time. Meet us in the parking lot tonight at midnight. And don't be late," he said. The next thing I knew, someone had punched me in the stomach and I was on the floor. "Yeah, and don't tell anybody, or there is more where that came from." They all quietly walked out the door.

Great. Just great. Now what was I going to do? I couldn't believe what had just happened. It was only one o'clock in the afternoon and my whole life was ruined. I sat on the floor clutching my stomach, wondering what to do. I should call my dad. But then I would have to tell him about how I got fired. I could call my mom. But then she would know. Telling Mr. Blomish was out. He would figure I was lying to save my job. Beep. "All workers report back to the assembly line. You have five minutes until the machines go back on." Beep.

I quickly got up and washed my face. At least now I had something to do. I could think about what I was going to do later.

Mr. Blomish came over at the end of my shift to remind me not to be late for my last day. "Is there any chance you could reconsider?" I asked him hopefully. He just looked at me, sadly shook his head and walked away. As I walked home, I thought, What would happen if I didn't show up? I would be beaten to a pulp. What if I went to the police? What would I say? I actually didn't even know what the guys wanted. Maybe they weren't planning on robbing the plant. Maybe they needed my help for something else. Yeah, right.

I got to the parking lot at exactly eleven o'clock. I looked around and but couldn't see the three guys that I was supposed to be meeting. I was so happy I felt like screaming. I thought to myself, "They're not coming. I'm home free, I will probably never see them again. They're not coming!" But as soon as I turned around to leave, someone stepped out of the shadows.

All three had black ski masks on, so I couldn't tell who was who. They each were carrying huge bags and one of them had a crowbar. I was now positive what they were going to do and I did not want to be a part of it. They were going to rob Mr. Blomish's factory and there was nothing I could do about it.

The fact that I was about to become a criminal was the only thing on my mind as they pried open the door. One of them pushed me inside and I almost fell down. It was really strange to be in the factory when no one was there. It was eerily silent and black as night inside the icy cold factory. The largest guy who I am pretty sure was Larry the Boss whispered loudly to me, "Where do they keep the finished stuff?"

I was so scared I couldn't even talk. He grabbed my shirt and shook me hard. "Show us where the good stuff is, you little creep," he cackled. It took me a minute for my eyes to adjust to the darkness. Then I led them to the side room where all the finished computers were stored, ready to ship. That's when I remembered the alarm button. The building itself didn't have an alarm but this room had a special button to alert the Federal Express drivers whenever we had boxes to ship out. It made a large neon light go on outside the building. If I could hit the button, there was a good chance somebody would see it. Larry shoved a bag at me and told me to grab anything that was totally finished. I walked to the other side of the room and bent over the table. There was the button. I hit it as quietly as I could and stood up, putting a laptop into my bag.

Nothing happened. "Hurry up, you idiot," someone to my right said. I quickly grabbed another laptop and started down the aisle. That's when I heard it. The sound of sirens. I froze. "What the…" said Larry. Suddenly there was a flashlight on us and I turned to see two police officers with their guns raised. "Put the bags down and your hands up," said one officer. "NOW!" yelled the other one.

I abruptly dropped the bag and threw my hands in the air. A string of curses could be heard from the other three guys.

"Okay, keep your hands where I can see them. Your act is up," said the officer. Suddenly I felt my hands being pulled down and handcuffs attached to my wrists.

"Wait," I said, "I'm not with them."

"Yeah, right. Save it for the judge," said the officer. He roughly took my arm and led me to the police car. I sat in the back seat wondering what I was going to do now.

"Pretty young, aren't ya, kid?" the officer said as we pulled away from the factory. "How'd you get hooked up with those guys?" I just shook my head. He'd never believe me.

He took me to the station where I had to fill out this form asking me all kinds of questions. Was I suicidal? Did I have HIV/AIDS? I was photographed and fingerprinted. I felt like I was in a bad dream. They put me in a cell with another guy. Luckily, he was not another robber.

I sat in a corner on the floor. I tried not to look at anyone. I couldn't believe I was in jail. Finally I heard my name being called. "Billy Smith." Then the officer appeared at the cell door. I got up and scraped the dust off my butt.

"This way," he said. We walked down a long hall into a small room. There were my parents. My mom was crying and my dad looked madder than I had ever seen him.

"Okay, kid, I suggest you get a lawyer. You're due in court in a week," the officer said. I didn't think that my dad could get any madder than he already was, but once the officer spoke those words he exploded, "Officer, what did he do?" The officer frowned and said "Well, we found him with some other guys trying to rob a computer factory."

" Are you serious?" yelled my dad. "I can't believe this. Why would you do this, Billy?" I just shook my head unable to look at him. Before my dad could yell again, my mom said, "Come on, honey, we can talk about this at home."

"No, Marsha, I want to talk about this now." Then my dad grabbed me and started shaking me saying, "Why would you do this, son? I thought you were a good boy." A minute later he stopped shaking me and just stood there looking at me. After about twenty seconds of hard-core staring, he started hitting me, full out punching me. He hit me everywhere, in the face, in the legs and in the stomach, before the cops pulled him off me. They put him in the jail cell I had just come out of, and the cop told me I was free to go. I wish I had thanked him for saving me from my dad but I was just too shocked to speak.

One Week Later.

I got up and took a shower like I would on any other day, but today was no normal day. Today was the day that I would find out my sentencing, whether or not I would have to go to jail. Luckily, I was being tried as a minor because I was only sixteen. I turned on the shower and it was cold, but I didn't mind. I needed to wake up. It eventually got hotter and hotter, until it was so hot that I could no longer handle it. I turned it off and stepped out of the stall. After I was dry, I went into my room and saw that my mom had laid out my best clothes. I felt immediately depressed that she was being so nice to me. As I looked at myself in the mirror, I saw a boy staring back at me, a young man with black hair who looked sad and scared. He looked as if he had seen a lot in his life, but the boy in the mirror was not me. He was a criminal, and I knew that I didn't want to be him. I hoped there was some way I could get out of this huge mess I had gotten myself into,

The drive to the courthouse was awful. My mom didn't say a word, and I felt so ashamed of what I was putting her through. "Mom, do you still love me? I just want to know just in case I go to jail," I mumbled to her.

She replied with a scream. "Of course I love you, but I am so angry that you ruined my life and yours!"

"What the hell are you talking about?" I said, trying to stay calm.

"Listen, for starters, you were the reason we moved here and everything went downhill from there."

"How was I the reason you left Vietnam?"

"Your father and I came here to make a better life. We wanted YOU to have a better life. But you went and just threw it all away. And on top of that you made your father go to jail."

"How did I get Dad in jail? He was the one who abused me, and not to mention, you."

"Your father was not abusing you, he was just…"

"No, Mom, don't pretend that what Dad did to you and me was not wrong. This is not the first time he has hurt us." Then she broke down and agreed that Dad had an anger problem and we should probably take some time away from him. She sobbed that she didn't know how to stay away because he had always been there. She parked the car and we hugged for awhile. "Come on," she said. "Let's go see what they plan to do to you."

I was shaking when we entered the courtroom. My attorney was this woman I had met once. I don't think she believed me that I wasn't involved in the robbery by choice, but she told me everything would be okay. She and I went forward to a desk with two chairs.

The bailiff told everyone to "please rise." I thought this was weird but I stood up anyway. It was really scary, and I started to feel sick to my stomach. I thought I was going to throw up all over. Then the judge entered the room. After he sat down, everyone else sat down, and so did I, even though I had no idea what was going on. The judge called my name and my lawyer told me to stand, so I did. The next thing I knew they were asking me to tell only the truth and I had to put my hand on this Bible. After that, the judge read the list of the crimes I was being accused of. I just stood there and listened with my head down. I felt like crying. I still couldn't believe this was happening.

Then I had to go stand next to the judge.

For the first time, I noticed this man at a desk opposite where my lawyer was, and sitting next to him was Mr. Blomish. I stared at him, pleading with my eyes to forgive me, but he just glared back. Then the other lawyer started asking me all these questions. The first thing he asked me was, "Is it true that Mr. Blomish fired you on the day of the crime?" I replied with a simple, "Yes." Then he asked, "Is it true that you got mad at him and you yelled at him?" I hesitated, then explained, "Well, yes, but he yelled at me first, and I didn't think it was fair that he fired me. I still don't." Aggressively, the lawyer then barked, "So you decided to rob Mr. Blomish as payback for being fired?" I started to get mad. "No, I didn't rob Mr. Blomish! I was forced to! These guys mugged me in the bathroom and told me that if I didn't help them, then they would kill me."

"How convenient," the lawyer sneered as my lawyer jumped up and yelled, "Objection!" The judge looked at the other lawyer and said, "Watch it, counselor, we want to hear all sides of this."

I immediately began to feel better. Maybe the judge would listen to me after all. "All right then, what is your story?" asked the mean lawyer. So I spilled out everything including how I pushed the FedEx button alerting the police. After I finished, Mr. Blomish started whispering frantically to his lawyer. "Do you need a recess?" the judge asked impatiently. The other attorney said, "Yes, Your Honor, there may be some changes to our case." The judge tapped his gavel and said, "We will take a twenty-minute recess. Please be ready as I don't have all day."

I went down from the stand and asked my lawyer what was going on. She said she had no idea, that this was not a normal situation. She said we had to sit and wait to see what the prosecution was doing. That was the longest twenty minutes of my life. Finally the judge came back. The other attorney stood up and said, "The defendant, Mr. Blomish, has determined the FedEx button was indeed pushed, and he feels Billy must be telling the truth. At this time we ask for minimum sentencing."

I looked at my lawyer in disbelief. She had a small grin on her face but looked straight at the judge.

"Well, this is good news for you, young man," said the judge. "Please rise and I will deliver my sentence."

I quickly stood up. "Due to this being your first offense and the fact the defendant has decided not to press full charges, I will not sentence you to the detention center. However, you must realize what you did was very wrong. In spite of any threats made to you, you should have told someone what was going on. You could have told Mr. Blomish or your parents or even called the police yourself. You do understand that, don't you, Billy?"

"Yes, Sir," I said quietly.

"Okay, therefore I refer you to twenty-four community service hours at Urban ArtWorks. You must go there directly from school every day until your twenty-four hours are complete. If you violate any of their rules or I hear any negative feedback from them, I will send you straight to Juvenile Detention. Do you understand this?"

"Yes, Sir. Thank you, Sir," I said.

He tapped his gravel again and said, "Next case."

My lawyer gathered up all her paperwork as I stood in shock. I was free! I didn't have to go to jail after all. Maybe it does pay to tell the truth. I didn't realize I was holding my breath until my lawyer looked at me and laughed. "You can breathe now, it's all over." I gave her a big hug, then walked quickly to my mom. She had tears streaming down her face as she threw her arms around me. "Oh Billy, why didn't you tell me?" she whispered in my ear. I just grinned back and walked out of the courtroom.

"Wait up," said my lawyer. "We need to go over to ArtWorks and get you registered."

"Oh yeah, what is that?" I asked. "You got lucky," she replied. "Don't be late." Then she told me about the organization that changed my life.

It was 9:30 A.M. on the 23rd of May, three days after my sentencing, when I arrived at ArtWorks, and I was actually on time! The judge sentenced me to work six hours a day with a one-hour break for lunch. I had a long way to go, but I was determined to show everyone that I was a good guy.

The first job they gave me was to clean up garbage out on these streets called the Urban Art Corridor. At first I was mad that I had to do such a silly job, but as time passed I started thinking about what I was doing and how good the area looked. Then I started liking cleaning up garbage. I mean, I was really doing good for the world. I was making it cleaner, I was saving people and animals alike. I liked cleaning because it made me feel good inside. When I finished for the day, I was shocked to hear they thought that I was doing such a good job that they planned to try to find me a better job.

One of the head ladies named Lisa asked, "What are you good at?" I felt shy and replied "Well, I don't know." She asked me again, "What are you good at? Are you a good artist? Or maybe computers?"

I got so excited! Would I really be able to work with computers? So I told her, "Yeah, I'm good with computers." She sounded skeptical and said, "Oh, are you really?" I told her, "Yes, I really am!" and asked, "Would I be able to work with them?" Lisa said, "Yes, I think so. Tomorrow we will evaluate your skills."

I thanked her. I was so excited I ran all the way home. I would be working my dream job. I could not wait until the next day when I could work with computers again. But then I realized that I would no longer be helping the world. I would probably be working with computers for the rest of my time at ArtWorks. Computers were my first love, but my new love of cleaning the streets was unlike anything I had ever done before. With computers I could do anything. I'm the master. But when I was cleaning, I got a really great feeling helping the world. I thought about it all night. Before I went to sleep I decided to do computers and not tell Lisa that I would have liked to still clean up the streets.

The next morning, I had mixed feelings. I got to ArtWorks early because I was so excited. They were not ready for me yet, so I sat and waited. Finally, another lady came out. "Your name's Billy, right?"

Oh, no, I thought they changed their minds. I replied simply with a yes, and she told me her name was Sheila. She showed me the computer lab and I was astonished. There were rows and rows of computers. I thanked Sheila for giving me a chance and asked her what job I would be doing. She told me to show her my skills and that she would find a job for me from there. I sat down at a computer, and Sheila asked me to do a couple things, which I thought were a piece of cake. After I finished all the tasks, Sheila looked shocked. She told me that I was very good with computers and that she was a teacher part-time and would I be interested in being her assistant. "However, there is a down side," she said. "I only work part-time so if I you want to help me it would only take up half the day. I am sorry but you would have to spend the rest of the time picking up trash."

I looked at her astonished. I silently thanked God for answering all my prayers. This was perfect! I told Sheila I would love to work with her and thanked her over and over. I told her not to worry because I actually liked picking up the garbage because I saw the value of the job for the world. She laughed and said she totally understood the feeling. Then she shook my hand and said, "Welcome to ArtWorks, teacher!"

Billy ended up finishing his service hours two weeks early for good behavior. He was eligible to leave, but he didn't. He and Sheila started dating a couple weeks after Billy finished his service hours. After graduating from the university, he worked as a teacher for three years, then decided to go back to school and get his Master's degree in computer science. ArtWorks had completely turned his life around. After he graduated, Microsoft offered him a job for more money then he imagined possible. He got up the courage to ask Sheila to marry him after having dated for three years. They now have two children. He is happy and successful and attributes his life to ArtWorks.

And he still picks up trash to this day.

the Early Years, Administration

For any community association relying on volunteers, recruiting is very difficult. Everyone, it seems, is busy with other projects, jobs or whatever. To find committee members who believe in a concept like ours is even more difficult. Donna, Ron and I were, in fact, the committee. We each knew people who we thought might be interested in helping us. We tried to define our needs and then match them to individuals we knew. Easier said than done. We then invited these people to a meeting.

I was very concerned when I entered the meeting room lent to us by a local business within SODO. Donna was there but Ron hadn't yet arrived. We looked at each other, sat down in silence and waited. One by one, the volunteers entered. About fifteen minutes later, there were twelve people waiting to hear more.

One of those awaiting the start of the meeting was Roberta Saunders from the Department of Neighborhoods, to whom Ron and I had made the grant request and subsequent presentation a week earlier. Each proposal was assigned a project manager and she was ours.

Ron arrived, and before we began the more or less formal part of the meeting, Roberta gave us the news. "I'm here to tell all of you that ArtWorks has been granted its request for $80,000 in matching support for the creation of up to twelve murals along the Urban Art Corridor described in your proposal."

We all sat there somewhat stunned. Most didn't even know what she was talking about but Donna, Ron and I did. All we could do was look at each other. Finally, Donna started to clap her hands, joined by Ron and me, then all the others. Roberta stood up and slyly smiled at all of us. She would become a very good and supportive friend over the next few years. Needless to say, the rest of the meeting was something of an anticlimax. However, we did manage to form a strong committee of dedicated volunteers who said they would be willing to work on this brand new project in the City of Seattle.

When Roberta made her initial announcement, she used a phrase that described the physical locale along which the first art would be created: the Urban Art Corridor. Urban ArtWorks would later become the non-profit corporate name.

We asked the twelve members (ten stayed on) what area they wanted to work on and began the long process of implementation. We had the administrative committee for day-to-day activities; a committee to work on the by-laws and the 501(c)3 application to the IRS as a charitable entity; an art committee to approve mural designs and get approvals from property owners; and one to begin the search for an executive director, a staff person to actually run the program, additional staff as budget allows, and art mentors. The director would implement the mission that would be later defined, subject to approval of a board of directors.

All of these jobs were critical but time consuming, particularly because we were dealing with volunteers, most of whom worked for a living as well. We decided to meet again in two weeks. Well, two weeks turned into another two weeks, then another, then another. Our committees were working very hard to begin a program the likes of which Seattle and King County had never seen before.

Our target date to actually begin the first of twelve murals was June the following year, 1996.

Good Kids

An ArtWorks youth paints a mural for Costco with Seattle Councilmember Richard Conlin at SODO Business Association's Annual Meeting.

The Port of Seattle commissioned two Seattle Art Institute students to work with ArtWorks youth to produce this cartoon depiction of cargo terminal operations and the Port's role in fostering international trade.

History of Jazz Mural Series. Created to beautify and deter graffiti at the construction site of the new Washington Mutual Building in downtown Seattle.

The Seattle Seahawks Mural is 540 feet long and is the longest mural in the city of Seattle.

Stop Bullying Mural. A unique outreach program between ArtWorks and John Marshall Alternative School. Mural was created with the students to inspire respectful behavior among peers.

This mural was painted for Seattle Fire Department Ladder 14 in Seattle's SODO Business District. It was updated several years later for the 1st anniversary of 9/11 honoring the courage of firefighters everywhere.

The very first ArtWorks mural.

The "Big Head Mural" featured in the chapter entitled Burnt Umber, depicts a Mexican American woman, surrounded by both the American flag and the Mexican flag, in full traditional headdress. This mural celebrates the diversity and heritage of the American people.

This 40' x 16' mural on the Pacific Coast Feathers Building was created on twenty 4' x 8' plywood panels, painted on the floor of an old bagel warehouse and then reconstructed at the site.

ArtWorks youth, two from the Mural Program and one from the Youth Art
Advisory Committee.

2006 summer mural program participant works on detailing this youth designed 80' x 20' mural funded by Seattle Mayor's Office of Arts & Cultural Affairs.

This full city block mural series was created to beautify and deter graffiti at the construction location of the original Public Safety Building through the City of Seattle's Fleets & Facilities Department.

This Sheraton Hotel mural was created to beautify and deter graffiti while construction for hotel expansion was under way.

Hiring the Executive Director

As the other committees were meeting, Ron, Donna and I began the process to find a strong Executive Director. However, the unwritten law of job placement is that regardless of whom we found, that person would ultimately fail. The first person hired for an important new position not already established always does. Suffice it to say, I've been in a position of serious corporate responsibility as the second person hired for the job. That usually succeeds. There is something about that first one that simply doesn't work.

Our selection was no exception.

But, I'm getting ahead of my story. First, we had to hire someone in a short period of time. Ron, using his expertise, wrote and placed an ad in two area newspapers. Besides, running a Request for Qualifications (RFQ) ad was a requirement, as part of the city grant process.

We were all quite surprised by the response.

A total of sixty-five applications were received within ten days. Here was a rather low-paying job in a non-profit with absolutely no track record, drawing an inordinate amount of interest by some very well qualified individuals. Most had experience in non-profits, some extensive. Interestingly, too, most were female.

One afternoon, we met as a committee at a local brewing company's pub located within SODO. With root beers all around, we began the elimination process. Knowing what we knew at the time about what we expected, we eliminated over half the applicants that day—those clearly not qualified, right out of school or otherwise unsuitable, at least, in our opinion.

There were about thirty who seemed qualified. Since Donna had used the City's copy machines one evening, we each took a set of applicants to study in private. This, mind you, was before e-mail was widely used. Research like this was done by hand, so to speak.

With instructions to narrow it down to our choice of six, we met a few days later. Surprisingly, we were all pretty much in agreement. We ended up using a rating system (1 to 10) and came up with a final selection.

Using the conference room of one of the SODO members who was a project supporter, we scheduled an afternoon and early evening of interviews. Each lasted about forty-five minutes. We had pre-arranged questions but gave the prospects themselves plenty of time to ask questions and discuss handling of specific situations, dealing with community, youth, courts, and whatever was likely to occur.

We then discussed what we had heard, voted again, and after a couple of ballots, agreed on a single applicant. That person was called back for an in-depth interview, lasting about two hours. She was a graphic designer by trade with a great deal of work within the non-profit community.

Two weeks later, she was on contract as an independent contractor, which was a simpler way to get things started. This also meant that from a budget standpoint, we could minimize cost as well as direct specific hours toward our initial project using the city grant. Later on, she became full-time, along with other staffers.

More Administration

As with any business, it takes time to get things going. This is doubly hard for a non-profit, which deals with volunteers for the most part and has limited funds in most cases. ArtWorks was clearly not an exception to these fundamental tenets of non-profit administration.

The committees worked long and hard to take care of their responsibilities. Soon we were an official corporation, had a tax I. D. number and had applied for the tax-exempt status allowed to a 501(c)3 organization. That last part was a major undertaking. Fortunately, the person in charge of that committee had serious accounting experience and was able to fill out reams of forms with minimum difficulty. The major problem with that type of tax status is financial. It takes money in the bank, essentially when applying. We did not have it, and it took some doing to get some from the community in sufficient amounts just to qualify. We had some very large corporations within the SODO community we could draw upon for the necessary resources. Those relationships are critical for both our Business Association as well as for Art-Works' financial health. It was therefore a very good relationship, first with the SODO Business Association as the primary sponsor and, second, the business community in general. One sort of feeds off the other, particularly in the beginning.

the First Office/ Warehouse

Where do you do all that's needed to get such a mammoth project off the ground? Monica, our new Executive Director, had a small graphic studio located uptown, about three miles from the Urban Art Corridor. The SODO Business Association didn't even have a separate office, but was housed in my office when it wasn't being used for my duties at Process Heating Co.

In short, we needed space, and what's worse, we didn't even know how much we needed.

Monica had a good friend who worked for a SODO member, a major recycling firm. They also owned a number of nearby buildings that were used for both offices and storage of surplus equipment. After a couple of coffee times and a drink or two after work, maybe a dinner or two, magically, office space was offered to our brand new entity. It was a block from my office which meant that, yes, I would spend much time there working on all the details, along with Ron. We walked in for the first time only to find a large empty room. I don't know if we expected to find desks, chairs, filing cabinets, telephone, computer and whatever else you might expect in an office, but alas, none of that was there. But we did have space.

The next day, we were sitting on borrowed folding chairs and had card tables and an old scratched up filing cabinet that took not one, but two hard kicks to the side to open a drawer. It was a beginning.

Monica said, "I have a used computer at home that I could bring in until we can get a new one." It was there that afternoon, plugged in. Then Monica's friend came to visit. Soon after that, desks appeared as if by mover magic, as well as a table, chairs and other office furnishings.

"Oh, all right," I lamented. "I'll go see the used computer folks that joined the Association the other day. Maybe I can work out a trade or something." I returned with two computers that I hoped had enough capacity for our needs with minimum maintenance.

We were off and running.

As for staff, we all were part-time, but at least we had a place to work in and a chair on which to sit. We paid for phone lines and went to Goodwill for a couple of phones (total cost, $2.00). A few days later, we could communicate. Eventually, even send e-mails.

Back to staff. Ron was doing some outreach for a local community college, so he asked around for help. A few days later, he introduced us to Sarah, an intern from the college who wanted to be a special education teacher one day. Perfect! She worked three afternoons a week for us for minimum wage. We could justify paying her from the grant from the city. Same for Ron's time and part of Monica's contract ($25/hr).

Part of the space was devoted to "creative," where mural concepts and other necessary tools of the art trade could be spread out. Here murals would be designed and approved.

The SODO Business Association received pro bono accounting services for tracking taxes and the like from a firm that worked for one of its major members. Most large organizations provide pro bono services for no other reason than to "feel good." In this case, the firm provided necessary startup information, software and training in the fine art of bookkeeping. This was particularly important, because we planned to finalize our 501(c)3 status. The help was invaluable, and soon, we were totally operational...at least from an administrative standpoint.

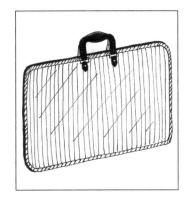

the Murals, Part I

Our mural projects required:

A wall facing on which the mural would appear;

Permission from the building owner to proceed;

The design;

Expenditures.

The canvas, so to speak, in our case, was to be on the back side of buildings that housed industrial companies in an exclusively industrial part of town. While these plants or warehouses faced regular streets, the back of them faced the busway and were seen by thousands of riders daily. Before ArtWorks, the "canvasses" were covered with graffiti, big-time. We secured twelve sides for painting, ranging in size from 30' high to over 500' in length. All were warehouse height, about 30'. Most were concrete or cement block. Under the often colorful graffiti was a dirty gray color. The surfaces had been neglected and likely not observed by anyone other than bus patrons, taggers and transients for, in some cases, maybe fifty years or so. In short, they were in pretty awful condition. "Pre" is just as important as "post" when it comes to murals.

Along the two-mile busway were sixty-five businesses, mostly in 30'-high warehouse- type buildings. A few were of corrugated steel. Some also rose to 50' or so. We began by selecting the sites we wanted to use, spaced out along the two miles.

Then the fun began.

Keep in mind, this was a new concept in public art, one that had never been done before. Therefore, the presentation was critical.

To create a graphic presentation, we employed the services of an architectural firm/planner, a member of the SODO Business Association. When we described what we wanted to do, they were more than willing to help. We told them we'd pay for materials but could not pay for their time. They said "okay."

After a series of meetings and site visits, we began the design process. We actually created mural designs from which building owners could choose. This way, they could say things like, "I like that idea. What if we did this..." Well, you get the picture. We weren't trying to deceive anyone but human nature being what it is and a spirit of community in there somewhere, they actually became part of the process. This would be critical later on, particularly when we were trying to sell other projects throughout the city.

Then came the part where we had to actually arrange appointments with the building/business owner to get permission to actually paint a mural on their property. This was at times a bit tricky, too, since in many cases the business owner was not the property owner. But we did the best we could, and at least got the ball rolling. We arranged meetings with whoever occupied the site. If more meetings were required, so be it.

Most, but not all, of the buildings were occupied by companies that were members of the SODO Business Association, a major assist. The first one was occupied by Cutter & Buck, a distributor of sporting type clothing, jackets, etc. They used the building for distribution of product, and when we visited them, they said they hadn't been on that side of the building for years. We showed them the back of their warehouse: solid graffiti on virtually all of the one thousand square feet of wall space. "Whoa!" exclaimed the manager. "Look at all that crap! How long has that been here? We had no idea it was like this. What is it you want to do?"

That was all we needed. The rest was just a matter of signing contracts (see Appendix) and creating the final design. Most of the other "selling" was the same. This was not the case with many mural spaces, but it was in this highly concentrated area of blight.

So, there we were. We had our first mural signed up and ready to go….we thought.

Next comes the creative process. It is important to have a committee, specifically a design review committee to sort through ideas and ultimately present them to the property owner—all this before actual painting can begin. We formed a committee of Monica, our designer and Executive Director; Ron, our consultant; myself, and our new intern who took notes. Monica translated our thoughts into a mural on paper. Nowadays, all this would be done digitally and possibly using Powerpoint-type presentations, etc. Back then, we did it pretty much by hand. The end result is the same, however.

So, armed with a portfolio of drawings, we headed back to the site and company management. Little did we know that the design was not the most important consideration.

The "selling" of the idea took all of three to five minutes.

"I love it" was all the general manager had to say. End of discussion.

Not really. Now the two questions for which we did not have answers: First, how will this be done and by whom, and second, and most important, how much will it cost?

Surprised, we made a feeble attempt to answer both questions.

To the first question, how, we said that we were going to contract with an organization called Streetsmart to create the mural.

They use young street kids for this type of project and their success rate with them is pretty good.

"But, do they know how to paint a mural?" was the obvious question.

Then, how much does a mural like this cost? Wall preparation, design, who pays the kids or organization responsible, supplies, supervision, administration, and the list goes on...

We had already contacted Streetsmart to see if there was interest on their part. Clearly there was, so we arranged to meet with the Executive Director who then joined the committee. That instilled in us the importance of partnerships on such a project. We'd find that more is better.

Then, the design. After several attempts, we came up with one that we all agreed on. Putting it on paper for presentation was easy.

Finally, the cost factor. Much more complex. Actually, since we were working on a large grant from the city for twelve murals, we thought that that was all there was to it. Not so. At about one thousand square feet each, the murals would cost much more than the $80,000, the amount of the grant. We decided to make the Cutter & Buck mural our prototype on which all other murals would be based. After we estimated all of the factors mentioned earlier, we then determined a cost per square foot for future murals. It came to about $20 for every square foot painted.

Obviously, larger ones would be more while the smaller ones less. Therefore, if we took the average into account, we'd be left with only $60,000 for eleven murals, clearly not enough. Should we make smaller murals or just do fewer? Neither of those were options as far as we were concerned. The answer is, again, partnerships.

We went back to Cutter & Buck and presented our estimates, laid out neatly in presentation folders along with the final designs. They were all broken out by categories and looked quite professional, if I do say so myself.

"Let me take this to my management and see what happens," the G.M. said. We were sure they would only give permission to use the space, not pay for it. However, as it turned out, they said later they would fund up to half the cost. Frankly, we were stunned.

After many rounds of thank you's, we took our leave to take the project to the next level, the actual doing part.

First, though, came the selling to the rest of the potential building owners/managers along the corridor. All of this was happening in the dead of winter. We had received our grant in November for projects to be created the following summer, when school is out and we would have plenty of physical support (more about that later).

By late February, we had all twelve sites selected, and funded! We look back on that achievement with a certain degree of awe. We had no idea that the community would step up like this. It almost became fun. Seriously, once a name of two was made part of the early presentation, well, quite frankly, they could not say no. Or, if they did, they had a good reason, like, "We're moving to the valley at the end of the month."

We only had two owners flat out say no.

I think you can see that the magic words for this type of project or when working with any non-profit are preparation and persistence. Maybe there is a third "p" word, prayer.

Nonetheless, we were almost home with what was to become the most unique art project ever accomplished in Seattle or the Pacific Northwest.

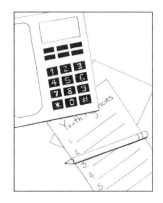

Murals, Part II

Armed with contracts for twelve murals to be completed during the three months when kids were not in school, or in most cases, not working, we set out to find how we could achieve this monumental task.

There were just the five of us. It became evident that we needed a plan. We needed bodies, more than could be supplied by Streetsmart, the organization made up of street kids with whom we contracted to do the first mural. No problem there. They might be able to do up to three of the murals during the three-month summer period. What about the other nine? Who would do them? Did they all need to be done during the summer? If not then, when? Then there was the question of supervision, overall coordination and management, not to mention supplies, transportation, and the list goes on.

We located five groups of kids willing to work with us. Five more murals for a total of eight. What to do for the remaining four?

Bad Kids, Good Kids, Part I

During our massive cleanup of the Corridor, the Department of Corrections provided as many as thirty trustees, who along with a much needed pickup, provided a major assist. Their supervisor told me about a new program being instituted by the King County Superior Court's Juvenile Court Division. Based on the success of the DOC program of assisting with community projects such as our cleanup, they had decided to experiment with similar projects involving juvenile offenders. He gave me the name of an individual who had been put in charge of this hybrid effort. He said they were looking for organizations to "hook up with."

Perfect, I thought. Now we could get four more murals painted using these youths. No problem. Little did I realize how this would ultimately impact the ArtWorks program.

Val had been with the Juvenile Detention Division within King County government for over twenty years. At first, he didn't know what I was talking about. It became clear to me that I needed to work on my presentation. Short of that, I arranged a meeting with him.

"Meet Monica, Val. Monica is our Executive Director and she's going to be our main liaison for these projects," I said, attempting to sound like we knew how this would all fit together. It apparently worked, because he started asking questions about us, our program, and how it would be integrated in what they were attempting to do with these kids who had gotten off the beaten path. It became evident that we were both attempting to justify programs not yet proven. A perfect match!

And it was just that.

Val told us after an hour and a half's discussion that he would talk to the presiding judge and others to see what could be done with this brand new concept. He appeared to like it.

The plan was for three programs from a half dozen or so being considered for summer projects. They would be prototypes for long-term cooperation.

A long week later, we received the call. We made the cut!

After several meetings with Val and his staff, as well as the remarkable presiding judge who was to oversee these fledgling efforts, we had our teams in place. Here's how it worked.

Ashley

"Just get out! Now!"

This isn't the first time I've heard these words. However, this time, I am prepared. I grab my bag stuffed with enough clothes for a week and about a hundred fifty dollars in savings, some of it stolen from Dad's "secret" stash.

I pull out my cell phone. "Hey, Jessie, I'm ready to come over, are you at home?" I say, trying to keep the quiver out of my voice.

"Yeah, come on over. There's a huge party tonight and it's starting in about two hours!"

"I take the 22, right?"

"Yeah it's the fastest. See you in a few." She clicks off.

I close my cell phone and walk out of my room and slowly down the stairs, glancing at the photographs on the wall. Mom, Dad, Ashley at the Lake '96, one reads; Ashley's first Christmas, another reads. Soon, I am at the outside door. I hear footsteps. Suddenly, my mom is standing by the stairwell.

"Ash, we didn't mean it, please stay. We promise to figure something out. Really, if you walk out that door you will be severely punished." I just stare at her. You are kidding, I say to myself; they care now that they know I'm taking them seriously? No, I'm leaving. I turn the knob on the door and step onto the porch.

Suddenly, I'm running. No, sprinting, down the sidewalk; houses fly past me. The 22 bus stop is about four blocks away from my house, and I am there in what felt like two seconds. I must be a sight: my dark brown disheveled hair flapping around my oval-shaped face, my gray eyes wild, red and dripping with tears. When the bus comes, I walk to the back and slump as far down into my seat as possible.

I finally arrive at Jessie's house. By then the red rims of my eyes have faded somewhat, and I pull my hair back into a messy bun.

"Oh Ashley! Honey, are you okay?" Jessie throws her arms around me and drags me inside.

"I should be used to this by now, you know?"

"Yeah, I am so sorry Ash, but I am always here for you."

"Of course, that's why I came here first."

"As if you had anywhere else to go…Just kidding!" I punch her jokingly on the shoulder and she gives me a huge hug. It feels nice to be loved.

"Ash, I'm dying to introduce you to this guy I met…he's friends with Byron and I think you would be perfect together!"

"Oh, Jess, I don't know if I can manage to dress up enough to even feel pretty right now."

"Oh my God, don't be ridiculous. You're always gorgeous!"

We laugh and land on her bed.

My name is Ashley Hamilton. I am fifteen years old and go to public high school with my best friend, Jessie Taylor. I live in Seattle, Washington, and have been living there all my life. My parents are both from Texas, where they met in college, but then they moved to Seattle. Then they made the mistake of not using a CONDOM and they got stuck with me. They got married, and I was brought into the world. Boy, did I feel loved!

My parents and I have…an interesting relationship. When I was born, apparently I was the happiest baby around. But by the time I turned eleven, my parents had decided that they were sick of having a child, and started to ignore me. I basically taught myself all I ever needed to know. I rode my bike to school, and once I got old enough, the bus. I spent all my time with my friends and their families. It never really occurred to me that my parents didn't love me; it was just that they didn't have any time for me.

When I started high school, everything changed. Jessie and I were still best friends, which we'd been since kindergarten, and our parents liked each other somewhat. But then my parents started thinking about having another baby. I thought, if these people can't even afford to take care of me, how can they possibly love two? Well, that's when the fighting started. It hit me badly. I thought they loved me. Then they told me the real truth of my birth: that I was just their little mistake. Wow, that hurt so much that I couldn't even go to school for three days! But what they said made sense; I could feel how they just didn't love me as much as parents should love their kids.

I kept insisting that they should love what they had. Wasn't I good enough? But my talk was useless. They had another baby. And my mother went through it all: the morning sickness, the weight gain, the cravings, everything. And they had a darling baby boy. Daniel was their amazing little savior, their little god. They spent night and day gawking at him. I turned into the evil one, the person who never even wanted the little adorable soul. After Daniel was born, things began to change.

Whenever I wanted to go out, they insisted that I stay home and help take care of Daniel, that he was the family now. I reminded them that I didn't want him in the first place, but they kept saying, "He's your brother! How could you not want him?" Well, of course I loved that little hairless freak. I loved to hold him and smell that baby smell. I loved to feed him his bottle and listen to the enormous burps. He loved me more than anyone, and both my parents knew that. But I wanted to have a normal life, and do normal teenage things. It was too late to try and make us a family. Well, after a certain point, my parents flat out refused to let me do anything.

I know they thought that if I did something bad, or wrong, that it would come back and somehow influence their little god-child. I told them they were being stupid. I told them that I was smarter than that and they didn't have to worry about me. I reminded them that if only they had spent time getting to know me, then they wouldn't have to worry. I was a good kid. But that made them snap. They kept saying to get out, and that they didn't want me anymore, and that they had wished they had taken the right precautions and never had me. That is how I wound up in Jessie's care, getting ready for some mystery party.

"Ooooh Ash, I am so excited!" Jessie whispered in my ear at the beginning of the party.

"I know! Me, too, and I can definitely use some excitement right now."

"Hey, you guys, what's up?" We turn around to find an extremely tall boy with intense blue eyes talking to us.

"Hey, Byron," purrs Jessie, as she slips her arm around his waist, "We want to parrrty!"

"Ha ha, I could have predicted that coming from you," Byron says, slipping her into his arms.

I let them have a little privacy and walk towards a group of people I hope I already know. They turn around and I realize that I don't. I turn towards Byron and Jessie, but they have already begun to party, alone. I sigh and walk towards some chairs along the wall. I pull out my cell phone and begin texting my other friend, David.

"Hey, you know Jessie, right?"

I look up to find this absolutely gorgeous-looking boy staring at me. "Yeah, how did you know?" I say.

"She pointed you out, and I figured that you, being the prettiest in the room, must be with her." He smiles.

My face flushes and I bat my eyelashes.

"So what's up?"

"Well, this party is kinda lame."

"I agree. But hey, there's nothing else to do."

"Well, that's not entirely true."

"How?"

"We can talk…and drink…and get to know each other."

"That doesn't sound too bad…"

He looks at me and smiles.

We start talking for a while. The gorgeous boy's name is Spencer. He goes to the rival school of mine. He's so cute, and we talk about everything: from school, to our summers, even to our previous relationships. Jessie and Byron come by, but we just kept talking anyway. Someone hands us two plastic blue cups filled with a mystery liquid.

"Finally, now we can party," Spencer says as he takes a gulp.

"Yeah, well after what happened tonight, I am totally ready. What happened?"

"Oh, my parents and I had a huge fight, but hopefully it'll all blow over."

"Hey, I know this is kind of off topic, but do you want to go outside for a second with me?"

"Sure."

"Sweet."

When we get outside, more people start to arrive, and the actual partying starts. Jessie and Byron play games with the mystery liquid, and soon both of them are smashed. Although at this point, the liquid isn't a big mystery… Spencer and I come back inside just in time. Someone turns on music really loud and Spencer and I get up and dance. It is crazy, and I have never had more fun in my life. I completely forget about my parents.

Spencer and I are getting pretty close. My head starts to spin and Spencer and I end up outside again.

"You wanna go upstairs with me?" he asks with glazed eyes.

Before I can answer, we are heading upstairs, where the bedrooms are. I am drunk and I know it, but I suddenly realize what is going on.

"Spencer, I want to go back downstairs," I say, starting to head towards the stairs.

"Come on, Ashley, you know as well as I do that we hit it off pretty well tonight."

"Yeah, well, here, I will give you my number and we can date, but I don't hook up. It's just stupid." I walk out of the room, furious.

I stand outside when Jessie and Byron come out all sweaty and red.

"You ready to go?" asks Jessie, with a flush in her cheeks.

"Yeah, what time is it?" I ask, hoping that it's at least past midnight so we can actually go to bed.

"It's one-thirty. Why, Ash, are you tired?" she asks in a mocking tone.

"No, it's just that I want to get at least some sleep..."

"Yeah, me, too, plus we have tons to talk about!" She winks at Spencer, who's appeared next to Byron. He pulls me aside.

"Look, I'm really sorry about what I did back there, that wasn't me. I had too much to drink, and I really would like to get to know you...you said I could have your number?"

"Hmm. Well, fine. Just sober up." I give him my number and Jessie says good-bye to Byron.

"Ha ha, 'bye girls!" Byron leans in and gives me a quick hug before kissing Jessie good-bye.

"I'll call you, okay, Ashley?" Spencer asks a playful gleam in his eye.

"Okay. Whatever," I say, suddenly feeling really tired.

As we make our way back to Jessie's place, my mind is racing.

"Ash, you're so quiet, what's up?" asks Jessie.

"He's really cute. But he tried to make a move on me. It was stupid. He took me upstairs." I sound lame, but I really am not that kind of girl.

"What an a-hole! Well, he sounded sorry, maybe you should give him a chance."

"Maybe."

"Nothing happened, right?"

"He kissed me, but that's it."

"I'm sorry I left you. Byron and I had a great time."

"Well, at least one of us did."

"Hey, you did meet a cute guy, and I told you, you would."

"Yeah, well…I didn't exactly want to be so lame like that."

"Ash, that took guts, and that's probably why he's interested in you."

We get back to her place and settle down to sleep.

The next morning, I wake up to find that my phone has three new messages. The shocking thing is, none from my family. They are all from the boy I met last night. One is an apology, another is just to say hi, and the last one is to invite me to hang out with him today. After breakfast I tell Jessie.

"Wow, he's committed! Well, I think we should go and hang with him."

"Hey, Jess? Today's Sarah's recital! You can't go anywhere!" says Jessie's mom. "You can go too, Ashley, if you want, but Jessie needs to go. It's Sarah's last year doing ballet."

"It's okay, Mrs. Taylor. I totally understand. I want Jessie to go to see Sarah perform and tell me all about it." I say to her, with a playful grin on my face.

"Whose side are you on anyway, Ash?" Jessie says.

"Jessiiieee! I love you! Come, LOOK! See my dance! Look at my tutu! It's PINK!" screams Jessie's three-year old sister,

Sarah. She spins round and round, in a blue leotard and a powder pink tutu.

"Aw, she's so cute, how could you miss that?" I say to Jessie.

"What? You WANT to go all alone to see that guy again?"

She has a point there, do I want to? I think to myself. "Well I guess not…I will call him back and see what we are going to do first."

"But don't blame me if he's a pervert."

"Thanks. It's great to know you have my back."

"You are totally welcome." She smiles.

I sit alone in Jessie's bedroom. She's in the shower, and I want to take this time to call Spencer, while I am totally alone. I debate with myself. He obviously likes me, but maybe he's trouble. I really don't know that much about him. Finally I call him.

"Hi, is this Spencer?" I say trying to keep my voice steady. I always get nervous when I call people.

"Yeah, hey, what's up?" he says, nonchalant.

"I got your message…messages… and I can hang out today, except Jessie can't come…"

"Oh, well my friends can come with us."

"Do you know what we are going to do?"

"Yeah, but it's a surprise. And bring some money; we are going to go eat at this really awesome place."

"What time?"

"In about…four hours?"

"I'll pick you up. At Jessie's, right?"

"Yeah, um, where are we going?"

"The Space Needle."

"Okay. We'll talk to you later."

There isn't much to do near the Space Needle. I mean, there are tons of restaurants, but besides that…oh maybe we are going to a play? Well, I am excited now. As soon as Jessie gets out of the shower, I get in and contemplate what I am going to wear.

"You promise you are going to call me like…every minute?" Jessie says when she and her family are leaving for the recital.

"I will text you about every movement I make," I promise.

"All right. Don't do anything I wouldn't do."

"Ha ha, which isn't much," I joke. Jessie gives me a hug good-bye.

I am really nervous now. I keep pacing across the living room, not knowing what to do with myself. All too soon there's a knock on the door, and I grab my things and head out with Spencer.

When we arrive at the Space Needle, I am totally bummed. What is there to do there, anyway? Besides look at it with awe, and take pictures, and people watch, there is nothing. But Spencer takes me to the Seattle Center, and we walk around and talk, and ride on the rides and play games. I was expecting him to be a self-absorbed cocaine abuser, but he is a really sweet guy. We eat at the Seattle Center, and we go up into the Space Needle and watch the sunset. It is my perfect date.

When it comes to an end, Spencer runs into some people he knows. Scary-looking people. Apparently he made arrangements to meet up and do something that night. Spencer says they can still do it, and that I can help them.

So these intimidating-looking guys, Spencer, and I all pile into Spencer's car and we drive to this deserted part of town. I am really confused until I see one of the guys pull out a spray can. Then the other one grabs a bag full of spray cans of paint. They are tagging buildings. I don't know why, or who will do it, all I know is I am scared.

"She won't tell on us, will she?" one of the guys asks Spencer.

"No, man, she's my girl; she wouldn't do that to me," says Spencer, and he wraps his arm around my waist.

I am confused at this point. Tagging is illegal, and if the cops come, we could get into serious trouble. But then again, I really like Spencer, and these are his friends, so maybe I should just go along with it. Besides, I can always tell Spencer later that it makes me uncomfortable.

Spencer and his friends take their spray colors of blue, green, and orange, and they start making graffiti. It's actually pretty, and they eventually ask me to join. I take the blue spray can and draw exactly what they tell me to. I swirl and dip and zigzag throughout my portion of the wall. Some of the guys start to comment. They say I'm good. Really good. One guy even tells me to finish his. I blush. I've never done graffiti before, I tell them, but they don't believe me. I am truly flattered. No one has ever really complimented me before, especially on art. For once, I am actually good at something, and can be recognized for it. It feels great. I run out of paint, because I was using the leftovers of someone else's can. Spencer tells me that we can come back and finish my portion. By the time we are done, it's amazing. It swirls and pops against the brick building. Too bad it's on a building, though.

Spencer's friends say good-bye and they take the bus back to the Space Needle. Spencer and I talk about what happened.

"Hey, you are really good at that. I didn't know you were an artist."

"I didn't either, actually. I was a little uncomfortable at first, but then it was okay. I kind of liked it."

"Yeah, well, we do our sign like that all over. We just hit down by the Port last weekend. Next weekend we are heading over to the freeway. It's going to be our biggest one yet. You should totally come."

"Really? That would be so cool!"

"You deserve it; the guys were really impressed with you."

I blush. Just as we pull into my driveway, Spencer asks if I would be his girlfriend. Of course, I say yes. I haven't known him for long, but I feel that we are going to see a lot of each other for the next few weeks.

"What happened?" screams Jessie as soon as I walk to the door.

"Nothing. Well, actually…I have a boyfriend!" I squeal.

"Ha ha, you are so cute. What did you guys do? Where did you go? Was it fun? Did you meet his friends?"

"Whoa, slow down! Are your parents home?"

"No, they went out to dinner with your parents actually."

I look down at my shoes. "Oh."

"I couldn't say no, I mean, maybe they just want to talk. You know, parent stuff."

"Maybe."

"Anyway, you are going to stay at my house as long as you can, okay?"

"That might not be much longer…"

"Don't say that. It will be." She smiles and brings me inside.

We talk about my day, and how wonderful it is that I have a boyfriend now, and how he is so perfect for me. The only part of my wonderful day I leave out is the graffiti. She would never go for that. It's wrong, and I know it, but it was so exciting, so wrong, but so invigorating and I still can't believe that I made such beautiful artwork. I have never been an artist. I've never really been good at anything, and to get so much praise… My day was perfect, my life is perfect now. And nothing, especially my parents, is going to stop that.

I am on the phone with Spencer. We are talking nonsense, literally, but we are also planning our days for next weekend. Then, I hear Jessie's voice in the next room talking to her parents. I hang up with Spencer.

"You can't do that to her! To me! What kind of technique is that! Leaving her! Tough love! There is no such thing! She needs me right now, and if you won't help her then I will!" Jessie is screaming now.

"Jessie, love, calm down, it's nothing serious; it's just that I don't want to be a part of this war between Ashley and her parents. She needs to learn that her parents really do care, but the only way she will is if she goes back home, and right now, we really don't have room for another person. Yes, she can come spend weekends with us, but she needs to find somewhere else to live, and eventually it will be her own home," says her mom with a desperate tone.

"Mom, would you do that to me? Would you just let me leave, not knowing if I would ever come back? Not knowing where I slept at night, not knowing how I made my money, or bought my clothes? Or even if I was getting a square meal a day?"

"Jessie, it's going to be okay! Ashley is a smart girl, and even she will admit her wrongs and go back to her parents. She is only fifteen. She has another three years before she can move out. Right now, we are not helping. So go and tell her to pack her things and that she needs to find somewhere else to stay for the next few days. Okay?" Then her dad says, "That's final, young lady."

"You know what? Fine! Be this way. And when you see that Ashley's parents aren't really doing anything but brainwashing you with this 'tough love' thing, you have to admit you were wrong and I was right. Okay?"

"Just go and tell her."

Jessie walks into the room to find me already packed and tight-lipped. She gives me a hug, and says she's sorry, and we both get ready for bed.

I don't sleep. I keep thinking and thinking about where I am going to go, what I am going to tell Spencer, and how I am going to get there. I immediately think of the park that is three blocks from Jessie's house. I could sleep and shower there, because of the community center, and I could get food from Jessie and Spencer. It would all work out. Maybe I could get a job, too. There's the ice cream store down the road that would hire me, especially since school is out in two weeks. Perfect.

I tell Jessie my plan first thing in the morning. She doesn't like it, but she says she will work with it. I call Spencer and tell him, too. He insists on me living with him, but I tell him that I am not ready yet, and that maybe I will, eventually. It feels good to have people care. It still hurts that my parents don't care. They want me to live on the streets. Well, they won't win. I am smarter than that. They can live in harmony with little Daniel and have the time of their lives, with one less thing to worry about.

After I set my stuff up at the park, it's another few hours until Spencer comes. I have nothing to do. That's when I have an idea. I had taken a spray can I found at Jessie's house for memory's sake. That's what I told myself. Now I have time on my hands, so I grab the can and take the bus over to where my unfinished graffiti is. I start to spray and to finish my work. It is exhilarating. Of course, no one knows what I am doing. I try to look innocent, but it feels like I am on a rollercoaster. My stomach is twisting and turning, my mind racing.

Constantly, I make sure the coast is clear. My blue spiky flower looks amazing. It makes the whole wall pop with color and draws attention. That's when I see the cops coming. I don't know what to do; I didn't think that could happen to me. I'm a good kid! Yeah, I have had my fair share of getting drunk, and I've been to parties with alcohol, but I have never gotten in trouble with the cops. I am terrified. What will happen? Where will I go? Will I go to jail? Oh my God, what is Jessie going to think? What about Spencer? My mind is racing faster than my feet can carry me. I get totally winded, I never was much of a runner. The police catch up to me and put me under arrest for trespassing and property destruction. I start to cry. My eyes well up, and tears stream down my face.

"I didn't mean to. I didn't mean to…" I say over and over again.

The police put me in the back seat of the car, and I sob and cry more than I ever have before. The policemen say nothing, but they have sympathy in their eyes. I lean my head against the window and stare out of it, the tears rolling. Big thick ones streak my face, and blur my vision as the scenery passes.

It all goes by in a blur of tears and fear. I end up needing a law-yer, and I have to call my parents and tell them what happened.

It doesn't make matters any worse than they already were, but at least they come down for my trial. The policemen ask if I know what I have done, and of course, I say I do. And that I'm terribly sorry for what I had done, and wish that there were a way to repay them. Well, there is.

The Judge sentences me to doing two hundred hours of community service. I am assigned to some new program called Art-Works. It's for juveniles that need rehabilitation. Well. I guess I'm a juvenile now. It feels weird, because I have always been so good! They let me off easy, I guess, considering.

My parents are furious. They criticize me and tell me I'm so stupid. They keep asking questions like "What could've possibly been going through your mind when you were doing that?" and "Did you seriously think that that was okay to do?" They say I'm grounded for the rest of my life, and that I have to take care of Daniel every day after school until I graduate. I'm not allowed to go to a party ever again. They don't know about Spencer, but I'm not ever going to tell them.

I mutter to myself, Aw, I have to start working on my service hours tomorrow! That's crap! I have go straight from school over to ArtWorks and then go straight home and go to bed.

As soon as we are home, I march straight upstairs to my room and head towards the phone. I have two calls to make. One to Jessie, and one to Spencer, because they both would want to know my newly screwed up schedule.

Jessie's mom picks up the phone and yells up at Jessie.

"Hello?" Jessie asks with mild curiosity.

"Did you even have to ask who it was? You knew my trial was a few hours ago."

"Well, sorry, but I wanted to make sure it was you, and not Spencer. God, he's called me at least four times. You should've called him first, because he was really freaking out."

That answer made me stifle a giggle. It's so nice to know that my boyfriend cares so much...partially because it was his fault.

" I have to do two hundred service hours! With some stupid place called ArtWorks."

"Jeez, are you kidding me? That's a lot! Wow when do you start?"

"Tomorrow! I have to go straight after school so I can have my 'orientation'."

"Ah, we were going to go shopping tomorrow, too! God, when are you going to have time to do anything? Isn't this going to take up most of your life?" Jessie sounds more worried than I have been. "Well, it is partly Spencer's fault, and Ash, maybe he's not the guy you thought. I mean, tagging? What were you thinking?" Jessie's voice goes from quiet to louder by the end of that comment.

"Jess, are you kidding me? Why Spencer? He showed me a way I could be good at something, and you just shoot it down! How could you ever understand! You are good at most everything you try, and have a loving family and boyfriend supporting you every step of the way. I have no one. Spencer came into my life and showed me something to express myself. Something I was good at, too. I can't believe you!" I scream at Jessie.

"You always had and still have me," Jessie says quietly, with a little quiver in her voice. I can't tell why, but she sounds close to tears. Why should she be crying? If anyone, it should be me! I think.

"I'm going to go call Spencer now. I'll see you tomorrow." I hang up the phone before Jessie can make any other comments. I call Spencer, and he seems somewhat upset. He tells me he feels really guilty and that I shouldn't have gone alone, because the cops will always follow people who are alone. He's going to take me to and from ArtWorks every day. I feel loved once more. After I hang up, I go straight to bed, with thoughts of what this ArtWorks thing is going to be like tomorrow.

After school, Spencer drives me to ArtWorks. I carefully survey the place. It looks kind of old, but new at the same time. The door looks withered and used, but the walls surrounding it are decorated with different bright colors. I take one last look at Spencer and step inside.

"Hi, are you Ashley?" a lady dressed in a stained white T-shirt and jeans asks me.

"Yeah," I say without any confidence in my voice.

"Your mentor is over there." She points to a tall woman by a shelf of what looks like paint supplies.

I walk towards the woman and say, "Hi, um, I'm Ashley."

"Hello, I'm Jordan. Are you ready for your orientation?" She studies me as I was just studying her.

"Uh, I guess," I say, as she takes me into the back room.

Tonight I eat dinner in silence. The day's events run over and over again through my mind. After Jordan took me into the room, we watched a video about a boy who had been caught stealing, and how the judge sent him to ArtWorks, and he ended up loving it so much he now volunteers there. By the end of my day I had a pretty good opinion of ArtWorks. It was a place that taught kids how to use their energy into creating things that people actually want to look at. ArtWorks. Jordan showed me some of the projects they were working on. All I saw were bits and pieces of the huge mural, but it was lovely. The colors all blended together, and the drawings were near perfection. The colors showed happiness and joy, while the spray paint had resulted in shallow, scrawled images. One can't compare ArtWorks' masterpieces to amateur graffiti.

I start to wonder if maybe some of the people who are working there for service got caught on purpose. I think this because Jordan told me stories of people she's helped in the past. Some of them repeated the offense, and were sent straight back there again.

Others, like the boy in the video, just stayed on to help others who were lost like them.

Jordan told me she came to ArtWorks because she wanted to help Seattle's youth. I thought she was joking but her face said she wasn't. Who really wants to help dangerous kids? Why didn't she want to stay at home and take care of her kids, or go and volunteer at some children's school, if she wants to help the "youth of Seattle"? But what she said struck a chord with me. Jordan wasn't helping me because someone told her to. She was helping me because she wanted to. At least I knew I wasn't a charity case, and that I wouldn't be looked down upon. In fact, I am actually starting my two hundred hours tomorrow. I wonder what they are going to have me do.

The next day starts off the same, Spencer takes me there after school and I meet Jordan at the same corner as yesterday. This time Jordan is dressed in shabby-looking clothes. "Today we are going to start cleaning the Corridor. We are putting some new murals down there, and we don't want it to be all dirty."

"Ew, why? Why can't I help paint?" I ask, trying not to whine.

"Because," Jordan says simply. "You need to start at the low jobs first. Don't worry, you will eventually paint, but you need to do the hard labor first."

"Fine," I say as I stare at the ground.

Jordan and I walk a few blocks over and we reach a long stretch of dirty streets.

"This is where we are cleaning? Only us? Are you kidding me?" I ask, looking down the streets in disbelief. I can't imagine having a worse afternoon—spending hours of backbreaking work to clean up the area around the murals.

Jordan and I are eventually joined by a few scary-looking boys, but we work in silence until I get fed up and start talking with Jordan. Soon the boys join our conversation and it makes the work seem to go faster. Two of the four boys were caught shoplifting, while another was caught with drugs at school, and the last one hot-wired a car. We trade stories of our arrest and trial. Mine was the most uneventful. It makes me somewhat proud; I mean, I didn't really do anything that wrong. Yeah, I was vandalizing, but it happens all the time. What about people who don't pick up their candy wrappers? At least mine had some color, and would eventually go away. But tobacco butts never go away. I learn that today as I pick up what seems like thousands of cigarette butts. It is gross, dirty work, but I deserve it because tagging is wrong. There is no way around it.

By the end of the day, I am sore, dirty and tired. After I finish my homework, I go straight to bed. I feel disgusting, and it makes me wish that Spencer didn't insist on picking me up every day.

Every day continues like this for a few weeks, until one Saturday afternoon. "Hey Ash, come over here," Jordan says as she steers me towards our usual meeting spot.

"What's up? I thought we were cleaning again."

"No, I think you have proved yourself. Today we are going to paint," Jordan says, with a gleaming smile.

"Are you kidding? I'm finally painting?" I look at the shelf. It's piled high with colors and brushes and paper and many supplies I didn't think I would ever use.

Jordan hands me a painting smock and shows me to another room on the next floor. A few kids are sitting at a table. As soon as we are seated, the woman from my first day comes through the door. "Look here! We have another artist: Ashley, right?" She smiles at me.

"Yeah," I mumble softly. The other kids look at me. There are four girls and four guys, counting me. Most of them seem between fifteen and eighteen. Some of the boys wear hardened expressions, and some of the girls, but still I wonder whether they are offenders like me.

"We are painting on the northeast section of the Corridor," the woman says, interrupting my thoughts. "A Seahawks mural. It was created by Tony, who is seated here, and since he designed it, he's going to help you guys actually paint it. Most of us here know the process of painting, but just in case you don't...it's an extremely long process."

The woman explains. First, they assign the groups of people, and then each group takes a piece of the painting. From then on, each group has a leader that reports back to either Tony or the woman, Dolores. Once each group outlines what their section is going to look like, we are allowed to make a trip to the scene to measure out the area. Then we sketch it, get the approval, and finally the actual painting begins. It would take a while, but I was excited. I couldn't wait to start!

The painting took months, and by the time it was done, I only had a couple more days left of my service. The mural was gorgeous. Or as gorgeous as a painting on a wall could be. Staring at all my friends' and my hard work made me realize this was art, not graffiti that takes only a few minutes to destroy the cleanliness of a building's wall. This art would be admired by people from all over Seattle. Parents wouldn't have to tell their children that it's not okay to do that on the wall, like graffiti; it encourages people to want to volunteer!

Being in ArtWorks for such a long time as a requirement makes me look at my world a little differently. I now see the beauty in things, instead of the sadness. Whenever I pass a street that is littered with trash, I try to pick up the pieces, knowing that it will help everyone, not just me. Whenever I see graffiti, I feel a pang of sympathy for the poor kids who put it there because they don't realize what damage they cause. Kids like me only think about themselves all the time, and they never realize that their actions might hurt those around them, too.

My family will never change, but I have learned to accept that. I know that they won't help me along the way, like Jessie's parents, or even Spencer's, but I know in the end, that it will have just made me stronger for my life to come.

I leave ArtWorks with a whole new vision: one of happiness, joy and hope. Jordan and I still talk. She kind of took me on as her daughter, teaching me so much more after ArtWorks.

After I graduate from high school, at the top of my class, she helps me move out of my parents' house and get my first job. Jordan is with me all throughout college, and we meet monthly to talk and learn from each other. Because ArtWorks has changed my life, I want to give back to them, so I volunteer, like Jordan does. At first, I just help with paperwork and organizing events, but then I start working directly with the kids. Some day I hope I can touch someone's life in the same way that ArtWorks touched mine: ArtWorks gave me new hope and love that I never knew in my life before, and they will be with me forever.

Bad Kids Good Kids,
Part II

We couldn't believe it! Seventy-five kids! We thought we were going to get maybe as many as ten kids for starters. The other eight groups were pretty much in charge of their projects, implementing the mural assigned to them. We actually didn't care how they did it. Everyone seems to have their own way of doing things and we didn't want to interfere. We were more concerned with the outcome, a great mural that would make us all proud. One group, in fact, was made up of fifty first, second and third graders. It was okay with us as long as they got the job done and nobody got hurt.

We established ground rules that made it clear that we were in charge, that we were to be, in effect, caseworkers or parole officers assigned to the kids. A terrific responsibility, but one we were willing to take. Monica and I both thought that this might be the start of something quite meaningful to the system as well as to the kids, their families and the community. We were not wrong.

There was to be adequate supervision. That meant a supervisor, later to be called "mentor," for every five or six kids. To take it a step further, that rule of thumb was established for all our projects and for all groups. So far, so good.

The kids would be paid for their work. What? Pay? We, as part of the budgeting process for our proposals, had included some funding for the groups involved. Some as little as $50 or $100; others higher, depending on the scope and the duration of the project. But, pay the kids for their work? Never. Or so we thought.

Our prototype assignment received funds from grants made available to the Juvenile Court, according to Val, the Youth Programs Supervisor for the King County Juvenile Detention Center.

The kids would be paid the equivalent of minimum wage, though we didn't call it that. Who knew? They were actually going to be paid for work accomplished, for community service time served, with earnings to go to victim restitution. Another first!

We also were to prepare progress reports for all assigned youth as well as a final assessment, on which their fate would be determined. These were the rules and we were ready to begin this most adventurous journey literally into unknown territory.

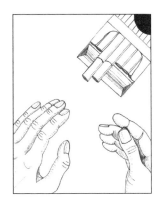

terrance

Betsy sighed.

From the window of her office into the studio space, she watched Terrance scowling at the other kids. His posture said it all: "Stay back if you know what's good for you." Slouched in his folding chair, he still managed to take up enough room for three people and scare everyone else to keep at least a two-seat distance. This was not a good start. Betsy glanced through his file again looking for any kind of hook she could use to cut Terrance's attitude back a notch or two, before things got out of hand.

Terrance had been sent to ArtWorks after a conviction of grand theft auto larceny that resulted in a sentence that was the equivalent of two hundred hours of community service, one of the longer terms for the program. Only the fact that his crime hadn't involved violence kept him from being eliminated as a candidate immediately. His file included a long list of accelerating crimes beginning with low-level shoplifting, moving up to petty burglary, and the recent theft of a car from a shopping mall's parking lot.

"Hey, we ready to start?" A head popped into Betsy's doorway. Jules, a black-haired charmer with a smile that could light a room, stepped in when he saw her expression. She nodded toward Terrance. "Just trying to figure out how to take Mr. Personality down a few pegs without making the intro all about him."

Jules agreed. "How about you and I double-team him, and let Chris take the introduction this time?"

"Double-team him? What do you mean?" Betsy asked.

"Just follow my lead." Jules went to the other team leader, a short girl wearing a bright yellow T-shirt that almost matched the color of her hair. "Chris, start things up while Betsy and I get Terrance situated." Betsy followed Jules to the row of chairs where Terrance sat. To get to the chair on the other side, Jules kicked Terrance's legs out of the way so quickly that the deed was done before the lanky teen had a chance to react. Betsy smiled and took a seat on the other side of Terrance, then leaned back to speak to Jules, forcing Terrance to remove his hands from the back of the chair. In five seconds they had effectively caged Terrance in. "I like taking turns with the intro, Jules," Betsy said. "This way, we get to see how it sounds from this side of the room."

"You mean, you get to hear how much it sucks," muttered Terrance into his chest.

Jules put one hand behind his ear, leaning into Terrance's personal space. "What's that, Youngster? I can't hear too good out of this ear. Too much of the rock and roll!" he practically shouted. Betsy laughed but Terrance just sat stone-faced. Inside, Betsy worried; this might be tougher than she thought.

Chris, in the meantime, quickly took the group through the basic introduction to the ArtWorks program and its mission. She reminded them of the various classes that were available in addition to their obligations. Among them are painting, basic writing skills, computer imaging and textile art. Through it all, Betsy kept an eye on Terrance. ArtWorks' rules weren't as severe as those of some community service programs, which restricted every minute of the day, but there couldn't be deviations without a good reason.

Regardless, every time Chris mentioned a new segment, Terrance responded negatively, by rolling his eyes, huffing disgustedly and scoffing outright. When the smoking ban was mentioned, he made as if he was getting up, saying under his breath but loud enough for Betsy to hear, "That does it. I'm outta here."

Betsy turned to face him, "Terrance, if you leave now, there is no coming back. Why don't you give it a chance before you write us off?"

Terrance stared back at her, not responding. Betsy kept her eyes steady but did not look away. Soon it was clear there was a battle of wills going on, and neither was going to back down. Jules jumped in, clapping Terrance on the shoulder. "My man, let's go outside and I'll show you the Smoker's Alley. Even Betsy wouldn't deny me a smoke every few hours. If—" he pushed his head between them, "—she knows what's good for her."

The staring contest a draw, Terrance got up without a word, walking to the back of the room. Jules put up a hand to forestall Betsy's comments. "Hold that thought. I'll be right back."

The rest of the class followed with their eyes as Terrance and Jules left the room. Betsy could see one boy whisper to the boy next to him, "How come he gets to leave?" while the other boy simply shrugged.

Chris, to her credit, didn't let the incident distract her from completing the introduction in her breezy cheerful style. All the kids loved Chris after a few minutes, seeing in her a kindred spirit who loved video games, manga animation and comics as much as they did. The fact that she could relate almost any situation to an episode of "The Simpsons" helped, as well. But, whenever Betsy tried to connect with the kids that way, they just looked at her as if she was speaking a foreign language. Betsy found that being herself was a much more reliable way to bond with the program kids. All of them had stories, some buried deep within. Her specialty was creating a space safe enough so that they could share their story without fear of intimidation, ridicule or disbelief. For every story that blew her mind—stories of pain, anguish, and experiences no child should ever have to face—she knew there was a kid who needed to stop holding that story in. Unfortunately, it often took weeks before that level of comfort was established. Until then, Betsy would have to make do, watching as Chris charmed the kids within minutes of meeting them.

Soon, Terrance and Jules returned, taking seats quietly in the back row. Betsy was heartened to see Terrance's storm-cloud expression had changed to one of calm acceptance. Once Chris had wrapped up, she gestured to Betsy and Jules. "Now, Jules, the hot dude in the dorky shorts will be leading the tour of our happy home. Go, Jules!"

Jules frowned at his paint-splattered shorts. "Hey, these are very cool. They're splattered in the style of Jackson Pollock. Who knows anything about Jackson Pollock?" he asked as he led the group down the hall to the studio space.

A small Latina smiled. "He's that guy who dribbled paint all over and called it art. And got away with it!"

Jules smiled. "He got away with it because he was good at it. I could dribble paint all day and never be as well known as Pollock."

Another girl spoke up, "Didn't he always name his paintings after numbers?"

"Not all of them," the first girl replied. "My favorite by him is called 'Autumn Rhythm.' Isn't that poetic?" She looked to Jules for confirmation, smug in her knowledge.

Jules agreed, adding, "Yes, but if you mean the one I think you mean, the full title is 'Autumn Rhythm, Number 30,' which would imply that there were twenty-nine other Autumn Rhythms."

As the group laughed, Betsy kept an eye on Terrance. Never did he smile, laugh or try to join the discussion. Instead he watched the other kids closely, as if sizing them up. At the end of the tour, Betsy took over. Back in the large warehouse space, she asked everyone to stand in a circle. From her pocket she brought out a small rubber handball.

"Okay, guys. Now we're going to do an ice breaker. Sort of a getting-to-know-you exercise." She smiled amid the groans erupting from around her. "I know, I know. But you guys are going to be working together here for a while and wouldn't it be nice to be able to know each other's names? Or at least the names of two other people? Here's how this one works. We all toss the ball, gently." She glanced at Terrance as she emphasized the word *gently*, "to someone across from us in the circle. They say to the person they tossed the ball to, 'Hello, I'm Betsy,' or whatever your name is. The person who catches the ball says, 'Hello, I'm Jules.' or whatever their name is. Then they toss the ball to someone new who hasn't had the ball yet and so on until everyone has introduced themselves to two other people. Clear?" She looked around the circle to see if everyone understood. Heads nodded all around.

Betsy gently tossed the ball to Terrance. Smiling broadly she exclaimed, "Hi, I'm Betsy!" wondering what kind of response she was going to get. To her surprise, Terrance merely caught the ball, quietly replied, "Hey, Betsy, I'm Terrance." He quickly glanced around the circle, then threw the ball to Jules. "Hey, I'm Terrance." The game continued until everyone had caught and tossed the ball through the circle twice.

Betsy caught the ball and held it. "Okay, quiz time. Anyone think they can go around the circle and tell us everyone's name?" She grinned as a look of apprehension went through the group. The girl who knew about Pollock, Tina, confidently raised her hand. But halfway through the list, she faltered. After a few more moments of silence, Jules nodded toward Terrance who appeared deep in thought, mouthing the names under his breath. "Terrance, I think you've got it. Give it a try." Without looking up, Terrance repeated the list of names in order. By the time he was halfway through, the group realized that he was going to do it. They started clapping and by the end, the room erupted into a cheering frenzy. Betsy hollered along with them, raising an eyebrow to Jules. Perhaps Terrance would be able to overcome her bad first impression of him.

Getting the kids' attention once again, Betsy led them to the lunch room. "Okay, that's enough for the morning. You have an hour for lunch. I hope you remembered to pack it. There isn't anywhere to buy lunch within twenty blocks, and we would prefer you to stay around the building."

Terrance asked, his face dark again, "But do we have to stay?"

Inwardly, Betsy scowled right back, "No, it's not a requirement, but be sure to be back in an hour. Like Chris said in the intro, lateness will not be tolerated. Being on time is part of the real world. No job is going to keep you if you stroll in late from lunch. And for the time being, you can consider this your job." She tried to address the whole group but felt Terrance's eyes bore into her the entire time. She hated sounding so stern so early in the program but the kids needed to know where they stood.

Jules, as always, lightened the mood. "Hey, I'm starving. Anybody want to trade for some sugar-free cookies? My girlfriend wants me to get more fiber, so she stuffs my lunch with bark and twigs. I need me some sugar, man." The group of kids followed him into the lunchroom, chatting amiably among themselves.

Betsy watched as Terrance made a beeline for two smaller boys near the back of the pack. Joey and Damian were some of the youngest in the group. Both had been sent to ArtWorks for minor charges: one for stealing a stop sign to put in his room, the other for breaking windows at an abandoned building in the industrial district not far away. Neither had any prior violations, and their sentences were some of the shortest in the group. Terrance whispered to Joey who glanced at Damian before nodding his head. The three boys left the lunchroom together. Betsy followed the boys as they went toward the front door. "Remember to be back in an hour, guys," she called out to them.

Joey and Damian nodded but it was Terrance who said sarcastically, "Yes, Mother."

Rather than rise to the bait, Betsy tried to take Jules' approach, joking back at the tall teenager, "That's a good boy, Sonny. See you later." It backfired. Terrance stopped in his tracks and slowly turned to face her. "Get this straight, lady." His tone was icy. "I am not your son."

Chastened, Betsy rushed to reassure him, "Terrance, I apologize. I didn't mean anything by it."

Growling, Terrance mumbled something she didn't understand but he was out the door before she could ask him to repeat it. It was probably better, she thought, that she didn't hear it. Sighing again, she retreated to her office, wondering how she could have gotten off to such a bad start in so short a time. True, there had been children in the program in the past who had taken some getting used to. Surly, defiant, arrogant. But rarely did they have all those qualities at once. Terrance defined "defensive" in his mannerisms and attitude. Betsy tried to recall how she dealt with it successfully before.

She was still struggling with this and her yogurt lid when Chris came into the office, plopped herself down in a chair and put her feet up on the desk. Betsy glared at the feet for a moment, the moment when the stubborn lid sprang free, splurting yellow yogurt all over the papers and folders in front of her. She jumped up. "Dang, dang and double dang!" she exclaimed. Before coming to the Art-Works program, Betsy's language was colorful to say the least. The Executive Director took her aside one day after her first week, explaining that she would need to clean up her vocabulary if she intended to stay. "When I overhear the kids asking what a word means, I know it's time for someone to tone it down a bit," she'd said laughing. From then on, Betsy developed a series of harmless expletives and sayings so antiquated and quaint that oftentimes the kids picked up on them and took them for their own. Many times a can of spilled paint was met with a lively, "Goodness gracious!" rather than the harsher vernacular the kids were used to.

Chris grinned, handing Betsy a napkin for the spill. "So what has you all tied up in knots today?"

Tossing the napkin into the garbage can, Betsy thought a moment before speaking. "Do you ever feel like sooner or later, no matter how good you are, no matter how much you love the program, no matter how hard you work, there are going to be kids you can't reach?"

"Nope," Chris said promptly. "The kid's not been born that I can't reach, given enough time. You worried about Terrance?"

Glumly Betsy nodded. "It shows that much?"

"Oh yeah," the blond replied. "You two clearly rub each other the wrong way."

"I don't get it. I treated him the same as every other kid."

Chris shook her head, "No, you didn't. You singled him out almost every chance you got. It was like you were daring him to be a jerk to you. And now you're surprised when he is one?"

Betsy was stunned. "I did? I didn't mean to."

"Now grant you, he started it with that chair thing, acting like he owned the place and was too cool to sit with the other kids. But you took the bait." Taking a bite of her apple, Chris continued. "You gotta ignore him for a while. Let him know that you don't give a fig what he does. Maybe then you'll both relax enough that you can work that mojo of yours on him and get into what makes him so angry." She stood. "Because that is one angry kid."

Leaving Betsy to her thoughts, Chris left. Betsy considered what the smaller woman had said. Chris had nailed it. For whatever reason, Terrance's attitude bothered Betsy more than she cared to admit. It wasn't that she was blind to the faults in the program itself. There was no such thing as the perfect program for every child, but her experience taught her that ArtWorks usually found some way to fit what they had to offer to every participant. She just needed to find the fit for Terrance. She resolved to concentrate more on observing than interacting with the boy, until she found how best to tailor to his particular needs.

Her good mood was short-lived. Doing a quick headcount when the group gathered to start the afternoon session, Betsy realized that they were three short. "Has anyone seen Terrance, Joey and Damian since lunch?"

Tina spoke up. "I saw them head out to Smoker's Alley a minute ago."

Jules winced. "I'll go get them."

But Betsy was determined. "No, Jules, you start these guys on the design process, and I'll go herd the last three in."

Turning the corner of the building, the sound of coughing guided her steps. Terrance stood grinning at the two smaller boys, one of whom was the source of the coughing, the other looking decidedly green.

"Okay, gentlemen, time to get started." She looked at Joey. "Are you feeling all right?"

Joey swallowed hard. "I'm fine," he said, quickly looking away.

She turned to the other boy. "Damian, was that you I heard coughing? You're not coming down with something, are you?"

The small boy tried to answer but was caught in another fit of coughing. Terrance laughed. "Boy just got some air in the wrong pipe?" heartily hitting Damian on the back. Damian's coughing fit over, he smiled weakly up at the older boy. "Yeah, Terrance. Wrong pipe. That's a good one."

Not liking where this was heading, Betsy forced a smile. "I just came out to let you know we're getting started with the design for the new murals. You don't want to be late your first day." She stopped Damian with a hand on his shoulder. "Damian, can I see you in my office for a second?" Without waiting for an answer, she reentered the building, fairly confident that the slender boy would follow. Her instinct was correct. When she sat down, there he was, standing in front of her desk, shifting from one foot to the other, looking for all the world like the cat who ate the canary.

"Don't worry, Damian," she reassured him. "You're not in any trouble. I just wanted to ask you something."

Relief flooded the boy's face. "Okay."

Betsy looked him in the eye, "Damian, do you smoke? That is," she smiled warmly, "before today?"

He shrugged, "Not exactly."

"Did Terrance give you the cigarettes?"

"Yeah, he was cool about it. I know some guys who charge you for singles."

"But did you ask him for it, or did he offer it to you first?" she asked.

Damian thought for a moment before answering slowly. "Well, he offered it. I told him I didn't smoke and he said there was no time like the present to get started."

"Uh uh." Betsy nodded. "And what about Joey? You knew him before you both came to ArtWorks. Did he smoke before, too?"

Joey laughed, "No way! His mom is really anti-smoking. I guess her aunt died of cancer or something, so she lectures him all the time about it."

"And how will she feel when she finds out he's been smoking?"

Damian was confident. "I don't think she'll ever find out. Joey would never smoke at home."

Betsy smiled back wanly, "But Damian, I can smell it on both of you right now. Cigarette smoke gets into your clothes, your hair, everything. After a while, even taking a shower doesn't help."

The panicked look was back now, "Oh man, Joey is so busted then."

"I might be able to help out with that. But back to you. If Terrance hadn't offered you a smoke, do you think you would have asked him for one today?"

"No, probably not."

"So that tells me you really don't want to get into smoking. Not to get all Nancy Reagan on you, but it is okay to just say no when someone offers you something you don't want." She leaned forward. "Be it a cigarette or some other drug. That's part of what ArtWorks is all about. Teaching you guys how to say no and mean it. And not look like a loser when you do it."

She nodded toward the door. "Can you send Joey in, and we'll figure out how to explain to his mom why her son came home smelling like an ashtray today?"

"Sure, Betsy. Uh, thanks." He smiled shyly at her as he went out the door.

She watched as Damian joined the group in the large work area. Terrance followed Joey with his eyes, as the smaller boy, no longer green in the face but still not looking too well, walked back to the office. Betsy found out that he too had never smoked before and had simply given into the peer pressure of Terrance. She reassured Joey that she would explain his cigarette smell to his mother in a roundabout way; that Joey had eaten lunch near Smoker's Alley. But that should he choose to smoke again, she would not cover for him in the future.

Joey grinned. "That's cool, Betsy. To tell you the truth, I didn't really like it. It made my head feel all fuzzy."

Betsy laughed along with him, "Be thankful that's all it did. The first time I smoked a cigarette, I threw up."

Joey made a face, "Gross!"

"Yeah, it was. But it convinced me never to do it again, that's for sure." Betsy forced herself to add, "On your way back, can you send Terrance in here?"

Where the two younger boys came into the office afraid and unsure, Terrance strolled in as though he hadn't a care in the world. Without speaking, he flung himself into a chair and stared at Betsy.

"Thanks, Terrance. Hey, can you do me a favor?"

His eyes narrowed suspiciously. "What favor?"

"Can you not offer cigarettes to the other kids? We'd rather they not start any bad habits they might have trouble breaking later."

"I thought you didn't have rules against smoking? Just against where we could smoke?"

"We do. But unless someone specifically asks you for one, could you keep them to yourself?"

Terrance smiled a dark smile. "But that isn't very generous, is it? I thought we were all supposed to be a team here."

"We are. And as such we should be watching out for each other's health. Not trying to instill habits that will wreck it."

"Jules smokes," the boy said defensively.

Betsy nodded. "I know. And he'll be the first one to tell you he wished he could quit. Plus, he's a grown man. Not," she looked him right in the eye, "a fourteen-year-old boy."

Terrance looked away. "Fine, whatever."

"You can go back to the design meeting, Terrance." She dismissed him, feeling her heart sink. This was one kid who was going to challenge everything she said, everything she asked of him. She just wasn't sure how to get through to him. But she wasn't going to give up, either.

Two days later, she began a life skills class with the group. This was one of her favorite parts of her job. The class was designed to help teach the kids how to interact in real world situations. They would write résumés, practice job interviews, learn basic computer skills, as well as the ins and outs of keeping a job.

Terrance spent most of the class playing solitaire, unaware that Betsy could log into any of the student computers to check their work at any time during the class. She calculated that for the sixty-minute class, he spent a total of nine minutes actually attempting the assignments. When she checked his time sheet for the day, she changed the time to reflect it.

The next day he stormed into her office. "What the hell is this?"

Betsy turned toward her mini-coffee machine and carefully poured another cup. "It's your time sheet. I corrected it." She set the cup down on her cluttered desk. "We don't give credit for playing solitaire, Terrance. You have to actually do the work."

He slammed the card down, causing her coffee to slosh out of the cup onto the pile of papers. "Fix it. Now!" he said menacingly.

Betsy grabbed a napkin and began dabbing up the spill. "Do the time working, and I will."

Terrance didn't move. In the reflection of the window to her office, Betsy could see his shoulders shaking with emotion. For a moment, she was afraid. Suddenly, Terrance reached down for the time card. Betsy managed not to flinch but also refused to look into the boy's eyes. The next moment, he was gone. She rose to shut the door and was not at all surprised to find that her hands were shaking. With a heavy sigh, she sank down into her chair and held her coffee cup close to her chest, breathing in the warm steam. Another battle down, but she was still unsure who would win the war.

In the weeks after, she tried to keep on an even keel with Terrance, watching as the group of younger boys gathering around him at lunch in Smoker's Alley grew, as his disrespect for the mentors and team leaders led him to question every instruction in his surly challenging tone, and as his mockery of the program itself lent itself to encouraging others in the group to also act out in negative behaviors. Finally, a meeting was called; surprisingly, not by Betsy, but by Jules.

"Okay, guys, what are we going to do? If we let Terrance continue the way he's been going, the whole group is going to be as lost as he is."

Chris spoke up. "I never thought I would see the day when I would say this, but he might have to go."

Betsy was shocked. Chris was the one who said there wasn't a kid born she couldn't reach. Betsy had been operating on the assumption that just because she couldn't reach Terrance, someone on the staff would be able to, sooner or later. It didn't occur to her that maybe she would be wrong.

Jules picked at the sole of his shoe. "Terrance is the first kid we've ever had to really discuss throwing out. I mean, for something not obvious. Remember that girl two summers ago we caught setting fires to the paint cans? That was obvious."

"No, this is different." Betsy agreed. "He's too subtle. It's not anything that he does, exactly. Nothing we can pin him on. It's his attitude. It's clear he doesn't want to be here. That's fine. We've dealt with that before. What I'm worried about is his effect on the other kids. He's dragging them along, too."

Chris nodded. "Yeah, he's almost like a leader but only in the negative sense. I had to tell Joey off the other day for slacking, and he just smirked at me. He looked just like Terrance."

"And I know Joey is a good kid. He just got caught doing something stupid to get sent here. But without Terrance egging him on, I think he would have made mentor," Jules replied.

Betsy took a deep breath. "Why don't we talk to him again, all together? Let him know he's on borrowed time. Then, if he continues to act out, he's gone."

"Let his actions dictate the consequences."

Jules ran a hand through his thick hair. "Sure, I guess. I hate to lose one."

Betsy smiled ruefully. "We didn't lose him. Yet."

The next day Jules brought Terrance into the conference room where Chris and Betsy were waiting. Terrance's attitude spoke volumes. He fell into a chair, leaning back as if he didn't have a care in the world. Jules spelled it out to him. "Dude, you are free to hate this program as much as you want. You can badmouth us behind our backs or to our faces as much as you need, but we aren't going away. We are in this for the long haul. What we can't have is you bringing the other kids down to your level."

Terrance smiled, enjoying the thought of control over the other program participants. He shrugged but said nothing.

Jules continued. "You have another hundred and fifty hours left to go, so you…"

Terrance jumped to his feet shouting, "One hundred and fifty hours! No way. I been comin' here for weeks now, more than fifty hours already!"

Betsy brought out his time card from his file. "No, Terrance, it's one hundred and fifty. I double checked this morning."

"You need to check your math, sister. You wrong!" Terrance snarled at her.

"It is not wrong," she reiterated. "When you spend the whole class playing games, we don't give you credit for being in the class. You can't just sit there the whole time watching the clock tick down. You have to participate."

"Forget you. I'll call my lawyer. You're ripping me off. This is some kind of scam."

Jules stepped around the table, "No Terrance. It's not. Now look, you have two options. You can either get with the program or you can leave. And by get with the program I mean, you show up on time, you do the work, you leave the other kids to their business. That's all."

"You can't make me stay away from the other kids. If we want to hang out, we can."

Betsy said quietly, "Yes we can. Tell me honestly, Terrance. If we let you stay, will you at least try?"

Terrance sneered at her, "Why should I?"

She looked around the room. Chris shook her head sadly. Jules stared out the window. Looking back at Terrance, Betsy said, "You shouldn't. Get your stuff. I'll notify the judge that you're out of the program."

Terrance stared back at her for a long moment. No one spoke. Finally Terrance walked to the door and flung it open. The whole building shook as the front door slammed behind him.

"Well, that's that." Betsy picked up the phone to call the judge and Terrance's county-appointed lawyer.

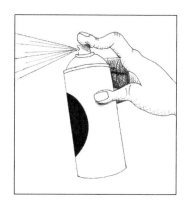

jake

P is for paint.

Jake sighed. He hated this part of the day; too early to think about getting out of here, but too late to skip going altogether. School wasn't his thing on a good day but today was harder than most. The conditions were perfect outside. A light breeze, slight cloud cover to obscure any shadows, cool temperature in the mid-sixties. Jake felt his index finger twitch. "I gotta get out of here," he thought to himself, wracking his brain for a plausible excuse to get out of the rest of his classes, nothing so desperate that the school secretary would feel compelled to call his parents but enough to release him for the day.

Staring blankly out the window, he let his mind wander to the small cardboard box hidden under an old camping tarp in the garage. His "Tool Box," he called it. Seven different colors, a mix of matte and glossy finishes, all he would need to create his next art project. All he needed was a space. He had been scouting some potential sites over on Capitol Hill near the community college. He found an auto body shop that closed every day at 6:00 and by 6:15 was empty. Little foot traffic in the evening, but enough during the day of college students coming and going to classes that his work would be seen. After all, why create art no one was ever going to see?

Finally, the bell rang. As he stuffed his math book and notebook into his backpack, he heard the teacher shout over the noise, "Pages 46-56 tonight, people. And Jake?"

Jake looked up at the slight balding man, wondering how a man who claimed to be thirty-four could look so old. "Yeah."

"I'm still waiting for yesterday and today's homework. See that everything gets turned in tomorrow. Okay, buddy?" Mr. Trains always thought if he called the students "buddy" or "dude," they would like him and be more likely to finish their assignments. In actuality, it simply gave more ammunition for ridicule.

Jake nodded and headed out the door. Lunch was his next period, and while he was waiting in the cafeteria line, the answer to his dilemma sat congealing under the warming lights. Teriyaki beef bites had been known to cause more than one student to turn incredible shades of green. He helped himself to two servings, ignoring the suspicious stares of the lunch lady. To further help his cause, he added green Jell-O™ so old it had lost its jiggle. If that didn't do the trick, nothing would.

As he sat down, his longtime friend and occasional girlfriend Angie asked incredulously, "Oh my god, you're not going to eat that?"

"Why not?"

"Like, because it'll kill you."

"Not totally." He stuffed a large piece of the brown meat into his mouth. Pretending to savor it, he mumbled through the food, "Mmm, Teriyaki-y."

"You are so gross. I don't even know why I sit with you." Angie sighed into the day's bag of carrots. All she ever seemed to eat was carrots. Jake often wondered why her skin didn't turn orange from betacarotene overload. Before he knew it, both the Jell-O™ and the beef bites were gone. He waited for some kind of reaction and was pleasantly rewarded by a loud rumbling from his stomach.

Angie looked smug. "See, I told you that stuff was dangerous."

Jake stood up. His stomach, however, flipped the opposite direction. Clutching his abdomen, he made sure the lunch monitor glanced his way before saying louder than strictly necessary, "Oh man, I think I'm gonna be sick." Everyone within hearing distance pulled back to give Jake plenty of room to get by. Tossing the empty paper trays, now stained a deep brown with leftover sauce, into the trash, he overheard a freshman cry, "That guy ate two teriyakis? Man, that's bold."

Once in the nurse's office, Jake tried to keep his expression one of discomfort, though in truth, other than the loud noises emanating from within, he felt fine. His mother claimed he had an iron constitution and she had always marveled at his ability to eat anything with no repercussions. But for now, he pretended that his stomach hurt enough to be sent home. After sending him to lie down on a wafer-thin, plastic mattress, the nurse took his temperature and offered him an antacid which he gratefully accepted. Ten minutes later, she checked on him again. "Any better, hon?" Unlike Mr. Stains' attempts to be friendly, the nurse's use of hon, baby and angel was actually appreciated by the student body and taken as the sincere forms of address they were intended to be.

Jake smiled wanly. "Not much. Can I go back to class anyway? I don't want to miss French."

That did the trick. The nurse hesitated. Most students by now would be trying for a home pass, but to actually ask to go back to class? That proved Jake was feeling poorly. "Sorry, Jake, I think it would be best for you to just go home. You still look a little peakish."

Stifling a grin, Jake tried to look forlorn as he made his way back to his locker. He calculated the amount of time it would take him to get to his house to retrieve his toolbox, then over to the site.

He should be able to get there by 2:30. Plenty of time to watch the foot traffic flow by and brainstorm for ideas of what to paint. He had a notion it should somehow relate to cars and the college. Maybe a character in a car wearing one of those flat graduation hats? He shook his head. No, it wasn't close enough to spring for that. Valentine's Day was just around the corner. A cupid driving a car? A cupid driving a car with a bag filled with pencils instead of arrows? Now he was getting somewhere. At last he had it. A cupid driving a car with a bag of pencils instead of arrows that he shoots at these hot babes as they walk by. Perfect. Now, to just wait for the auto shop to close and everyone to leave.

During the hours Jake waited for the coast to clear, he sketched his ideas onto the drawing pad he always carried with him. By the time 6:15 rolled around, he had page after page of intricate drawings all labeled with color suggestions in his neat block lettering. The streetlights had come on, casting a pale orange glow over the side of the building. He would have to remember to compensate for that as he went. Running a hand over the side of the building, Jake noticed a sheen of grime coming off that would have to be dealt with before he began painting. He pulled a rag from his backpack and a bottle of spray cleaner. He laughed to himself that even if someone did come along and find him, all they would find was a teenage boy cleaning a building. No crime in that. But to be on the safe side, he glanced around anyway. No one was there.

Quickly, with the ease of practice, he wiped away layer after layer of dirt until he had a patch roughly eight feet high and fifteen across. As he took the cans of spray paint from the box, Jake's heart began to pound. He loved this part the best. A whole new unmarked space, just waiting for his inspiration to adorn it. He cracked his knuckles and set to work. Vaguely he felt the spray mist back onto his face, hands and shirt. He breathed in the fumes deeply, enjoying the way it made his vision spin for a few seconds before returning to normal. In the back of his mind he made a mental note to add filter masks to his toolbox. No use getting brain damage like those kids in the "Huffing and You" video his health teacher made them watch a few weeks ago, all about the dangers of inhaling toxic substances like glue or hair spray. Jake never quite understood the siren song of drugs that called to some of his friends. Why deliberately disconnect from life? Why choose to feel sluggish and stupid when all it took was inspiration and creativity to feel incredible? Right now he felt on top of the world. His hand flew over the surface of the building, adding marks here, adjusting color there. It was as if his mind were going a mile a minute. He understood how DaVinci felt, creating a masterpiece.

Finally, though it felt like he had just begun, Jake stepped back and examined his work. The car, a cartoony red vehicle with balloon-like tires, was driven by a fat, cherubic Cupid with a wicked and jovial gleam in his eye. One chubby hand was fitting an enormous pencil into a militaristic crossbow aimed at a group of graphic novel-style girls with tight-fitting shorts and halter tops. Their proportions were exaggerated but comically enough for Jake to feel confident that no one could object that the depiction was sexist. And even if they did, who would they complain to? It wasn't like this was a gallery showing that could be picketed.

Jake gathered his supplies, taking time to clean off his stained hands with another rag. After one last look at his piece, he started walking down the street toward the bus stop, wishing he could skip school tomorrow just to sit on the corner and see the reaction of pedestrians going by.

His reverie was interrupted by a loud cough. Two people stepped out from the shadows saying, "All done?"

Jake looked up, startled from his day dream. He had thought he was alone on the street. His heart leapt in his chest as he saw the two were uniformed police officers, a man and a woman. Suddenly his palms felt damp on the straps of his backpack. "Excuse me?" he choked.

The female officer walked toward the painting as the man stepped closer to Jake. "I said, are you all done? Usually we don't have to wait this long for you taggers to finish up."

Jake's eyebrows furrowed, "Tagger? I'm not a tagger."

"Oh really?" the female cop gestured toward the building, "So what do you call this?"

"Art," Jake replied feeling much less haughty than he sounded. "Taggers are punks."

This brought a grin to the woman's face. "Are they? But you, you're an artist?" Clearly, she thought this was funny.

"At least I don't just scribble a bunch of gang junk all over. My art is—" He faltered trying to find the right word to describe his individual talent and style.

"Illegal," supplied the woman, laughing outright now. "Okay kid, drop the bag, put your hands behind your back and be prepared to be searched for weapons. It is in your best interest to not resist my instructions."

As Jake complied, his mind tried to find a way to explain everything to the officers. If they could just understand that what he was doing was art, then it would be all right. His contempt for taggers was true. All they did was vandalize buildings and make it harder for legitimate artists like himself to find space upon which to create. Surely if the officers would just look at the painting, they would see the difference. But they seemed oblivious to it. After they searched him and read him his rights, they carefully put him in the back seat of their car, parked around the corner from the auto shop. Before they went anywhere, however, the man got a digital camera from the trunk of the car and returned to the painting, taking several photos from various angles. Jake hoped that he could have some sent to his home computer once this was all straightened out. He had never thought to document his art before and resolved to bring a digital camera along next time.

Two hours later, his parents arrived. Seeing the expression on his father's face, Jake knew the police officers had not explained the situation properly.

"Dad—" he began but was cut off.

"I don't want to hear it, Jake. Do you have any idea how much trouble you're in right now?"

"It can't be that bad. All I did was paint a picture," he protested.

"All you did was about five thousand dollars in damage to a perfectly innocent local business! Why in the world did you think that defacing a building like that was acceptable behavior?"

Jake was stunned. Defacing? His father made it sound like he had ruined the building, not made it better. Or at least better to look at.

"Jake," his mother's voice was soft. He turned to face her. "Just tell us why you did it. Then maybe we can understand."

He tried to find the words to explain but all he could do was shrug helplessly. "I dunno."

His father sighed heavily, running a hand through his hair. "Well, for whatever reason you did this, now we have to deal with the consequences. The officer told us that you'll be released after you see the judge."

"Judge? What do I have to see a judge for?" Jake asked incredulously.

"Jake, you're charged with vandalism. That's a pretty serious offense. You didn't think you were just going to walk out of here and go home? This is way beyond getting grounded from X-Box for a week." Mr. Basher looked intently at his son, trying to convey the seriousness of the situation.

"But I didn't do anything!" Jake's voice rose in the small room. His mother took his hands. "Jake, are you telling me you didn't paint up that building? Honestly, now."

"No, I painted it, but I still don't see what's so terrible about that. Did the guy show you the picture he took of it? Maybe if you saw it, then you wouldn't be so harsh about it."

"Yes, Jake, the officer did show it to us and I must say I was surprised."

Jake grinned. "It was good, wasn't it? I was trying to—" His father cut him off.

"Good? No, Jake, it wasn't good. In fact it was sexist and rude and vulgar. I don't know where you got the idea that it was acceptable to portray women dressed like that or acting that way but it made me feel sick. We need to have a serious talk about the roles of women in society when we get home. Women are not just objects to be ogled at on the side of an auto shop." A hand on his arm kept Mr. Basher from continuing his rant but his point had been made.

A tall, dark-haired man entered, introducing himself as Glenn from King County Child Services. "Jake, I'm here to act as your lawyer, to make sure you understand the charges against you and possibilities for sentencing. Now, I assume you had time to talk this over with your folks. I've had a look at your file and I think I may have some options for you, if you're interested." When Jake nodded, he continued. "Well, there is a program designed for kids like you called ArtWorks. Have you ever heard of it? Rather than give them time in juvenile detention or regular community service, the court assigns kids to ArtWorks. In their program you can do a variety of things to fulfill your service obligations. For example, they often will do public art projects around town. Given your interest in artistic endeavors, this would give you a positive way to express yourself without getting into trouble with the courts. Sound good?" Glenn smiled when he saw the look on Jake's face.

Mr. Basher asked, "And this program would take care of his sentencing obligations, whatever they turn out to be?"

"Yes, it depends upon the judge signing off on it, but I see no reason he wouldn't. ArtWorks rarely gets turned down if the offender meets the requirements and it looks like Jake does."

"Now wait a sec," Jake said. "You mean I'm going to get stuck in some baby art class with a bunch of rejects and taggers? Cuz, in that case I'm not interested."

Glenn replied, "Actually Jake, ArtWorks takes all kinds of kids for all kinds of offenses, not just vandalism. There are some auto thieves, offenders who committed petty larceny, burglary, as well as taggers. You'll be surprised at who you meet. And the classes themselves are hardly 'baby classes.' They're taught and overseen by artists and art students from the schools around town."

Jake admitted this sounded better, though he wasn't sure how comfortable he was with the idea of spending a lot of time with criminals. But if it kept him from picking up litter on the side of the road, he was willing to give it a shot.

Jake's first impression of ArtWorks was not a positive one. The warehouse building was in a part of town he rarely visited and he got lost more than once on the way. His mother loaned him her car for the first day but made it clear not to get to used to the idea of driving. After today, he would take the bus. Once inside, he was startled to hear loud music blasting from a large open room filled with kids about his own age. They didn't seem to be working at all, just dancing around wildly. They revolved around a short girl wearing a ripped, paint-encrusted T-shirt dress and flip-flops. Her long red hair whirled around her as she spun in place to the cheers and claps of the kids in a circle around her. When the song ended, she fell into a heap on the concrete floor.

Glancing up, she noticed Jake still standing in the doorway. "Hi!" she called out enthusiastically. "You must be Jake."

When he nodded, she bellowed at him, "You're late!" Jumping up, she motioned the others toward a large table filled with drafting supplies, and bounded over.

Offering her hand, she said, "I'm Vicki, and if you're even a minute late again, you're out of the program. Clear? Good." Without waiting for a response she sped over to a desk and handed him a stack of papers to fill out. "We're a non-profit so we revolve around paperwork. Get used to it. Join us when you're done."

And with that, she skipped back to the group, cheerfully barking orders to the waiting teens.

Jake looked at the pile of papers. There had to be at least a dozen. "I thought I was here to learn something, not how to write my name a million times." At last he finished reading and signing all the various forms. After bringing them to the crowded drafting table, he waited for a break in the discussion but Vicki simply nodded toward a large plastic tray on the desk marked "In." Sighing at having wasted his time, he trudged back to the desk and dropped the pile atop the others.

At the drafting table he saw Vicki holding up a large sheet of what looked like architectural paper with light blue lines outlining the shape of a picture on a deeper blue background.

"Jake, tell me what you think of this composition." Vicki shoved the paper closer to him. Glancing at it, Jake said, "Well, the words are too hard to see, so either the type should be changed to a clearer one or at least made bigger. And it's hard to tell what the finished product is going to look like when it's all done in blues. And is that supposed to be a hippo or a rock?"

"Okay, group, who wants to tell Mr. Jake what he just did wrong?" Vicki asked. Every hand shot up in the air. She picked one, a round-headed guy with a large hoop earring in one ear. "Mario."

"Thanks, Vicki. Jake didn't introduce himself when he first came over."

"Good. Anyone else?"

"He didn't tell his opinion in the form of a compliment."

"Good. Anyone else?"

"He didn't—." Before the next speaker could finish, Jake spoke up harshly, "Hey wait a sec. I didn't know there were all these rules about comments. Vicki asked me what I thought and I told her."

Vicki smiled but there was something else in her face. "Jake, you didn't know because you didn't ask. Ever since you got here, you've been all rolling eyes and sighs." She rolled her eyes and sighed deeply, bringing one hand up to her head like a damsel in distress from an old silent movie. The other kids started wailing and moaning, clutching their hands to their hearts or laughing outright. This angered Jake even more. Who the heck were these losers to make fun of him? He started to walk toward to the door, prompting even more ridicule. Mario called out, "Hey, Quitter! You need to sign a form if you run out on us."

Vicki jogged over. "Jake, you are not getting off on the right foot. If you leave now, then your participation in this program is done. We don't have time for temper tantrums and we don't make exceptions for spoiled rich kids who got caught being stupid." She gave him a long look. "So what's it going to be? You want to try again and start the right way or you want to go to the judge and explain why you bailed after ten minutes?" When he hesitated, she turned away, "Okay, you had your chance but I don't ask twice."

"Fine, fine," Jake said quickly, "I'll stay. But can you at least cut me some slack? It is my first day, you know."

Vicki smiled. "No, I won't cut you any slack, especially since it's your first day. But I will show you the ropes. Come on and meet the crew."

The rest of the morning passed without further incident. Vicki introduced him to the other twelve members of his team and had each of them explain one rule of the program, such as showing up on time. Then they worked together to clarify the end result of the mural they wanted to paint on the side of a local underpass tunnel. At lunch, he sat with Mario on a picnic bench just outside the warehouse. It was chilly but the fresh air felt good after the rather stuffy air inside.

"So, Mario, do all the new kids have to learn the hard way like I did?" Jake asked.

"Only if they come in spouting attitude like you done. That's one of the things Vicki is always harping on." He imitated her squeaky high voice, "You only get one chance to make a first impression." Grinning, he added, "I never really knew what she meant until you came in here all scowly and angry."

Jake grinned back. "But see, all you had to do was get to know the fascinating specimen before you."

"Yeah, but you don't always get a chance to let people get to know you. Sometimes all they get is that first look, and if they don't like it, they ain't gonna give you a second chance. Like in Interview class, we did this role-playing thing where Vicki and another mentor, Bobbi, were pretending to be these total slacker dudes showing up for a job interview. We had to be the interview panel and they were all, like, using slang and dressed in shorts and ragged T-shirts. Vicki messed her hair all up so it looked like she never combed it and Bob had food stains all over his clothes. Everyone on the interview panel voted against hiring them, even though they all had great references and previous experience."

Jake laughed. "Sounds like me when I went to get a job at this coffee shop by my house last summer."

"But did you get the job?" Mario asked.

"No, but they were lame. I only went to get my dad off my back."

"Some of us aren't so lucky to have a dad, off our backs or not. I mean, if I ever want any spending money I gotta earn it myself. That's why those classes are important. We did the same situation again, only Vicki and Bob wore nice clothes and were respectful. They used, you know, proper English and stuff. This time, everyone voted to hire them, even though they changed their references to be not as good as the first time."

Jake thought about this. It made sense, though he would have to test it soon enough. His dad was already reminding him that he was expected to get a paying job this summer.

After the work day ended, Jake poked his head into Vicki's office. "Sorry about this morning. It won't happen again."

Without looking up, Vicki answered, "I know. See you on the flip side."

Six weeks into his eight-week sentence with ArtWorks, Jake was surprised to be called to the Dean's office at school. Gesturing to an armchair, Mr. Harper asked, "So Jake, how is the ArtWorks thing coming along? Almost finished?"

Jake was surprised. He didn't think anyone at school knew about his arrest and sentencing. "Okay, I guess." He tried to keep from mumbling but really didn't want to talk about the program with this relative stranger. Mr. Harper was well known as the school disciplinarian and a harsh one at that, with a "spare the rod and spoil the child" philosophy.

"Vicki says you're doing quite well in the painting group and that your mural is almost completed."

"Yeah, it should be done in a week or two. Then we're having an unveiling for the school kids. They're making a big deal out of it." Jake was surprised to feel a tingle of pride at the thought of the mural he and the rest of the crew had worked so hard to complete.

"As well they should. Well, then, that's fine. Since you're almost done with the program, perhaps you'd like to start on the time you need to complete here at school? It won't have to interfere with your ArtWorks time but we need to get it out of the way before the end of the school year."

Jake inwardly groaned. He had conveniently forgotten that when he was sentenced, the school informed his parents that he would be expected to do detention as well.

"Mr. Harper, maybe you can explain something to me?"

"Certainly, if I can." Mr. Harper leaned back in his chair.

"Why do I have to do detention here at school and do my time with ArtWorks? I mean, isn't that being punished twice for the same thing?"

Mr. Harper smiled a small smile under his bushy moustache. "Jake, the time you did with ArtWorks is to repay the city and the auto shop for the damage you did. The time you do with us is to repay the debt to the school for doing such a thing in the first place. We try here to instill in our students a sense of right and wrong, and although I think you know the difference, you deliberately did wrong anyway. So, you need to be punished for breaking the school's morality clause, if you will."

Jake managed to keep his temper but with difficulty. "I see. For the record, I still think that it's unfair. But I'll do it anyway."

"Might I suggest that you talk to Ms. Lee about using some of your new skills with a paintbrush to help paint sets for the school musical? The run should last just about the right amount of time."

"Great," Jake said, thinking, "now I can add Drama Geek to my new résumé. Bobbie would love it."

That afternoon, he knocked on the door to the drama teacher's small office. The tiny room looked like it was originally a closet but now the walls were covered with posters from past productions. Tidy stacks of scripts lined the desk. Ms. Lee looked up from a three-ring binder in which she was writing furiously. She was a brunette with sparkling white teeth slightly too big for her mouth and deeply furrowed laugh lines. "Oh Jake, good you're here. Mr. Harper warned me I might get a visit from you. Ready to become a techie?"

Jake swallowed nervously. It reminded him of one of the role plays he did with the Interview class, only this time it meant the difference between washing desks and lockers or doing something remotely interesting. "Techie?"

"A techie is one of the behind-the-scenes people who make all plays run smoothly. At least we hope so," she added.

"I get you. I guess so, then."

"Great! Now, I hear you like to work with paint."

At the thought, Jake's fingers felt a slight twitch, and he wished his parents hadn't made him throw his toolbox in the trash. "I sure do. Lately I've been working on this mural at an elementary school. It's going up on the side of one of their portables. We unveil it next week."

"That's about the scale we're talking about. The musical this year is The Music Man. Do you know it?"

"The one about the band guy and the librarian, right?"

Ms. Lee nodded. "I'm impressed, Jake. Do we have a secret musical theater fan in our midst?"

"No, but my mom is. She has, like, two versions of it on DVD and makes me watch them with her every Thanksgiving."

"That makes my job a little easier then." She handed him some rough drawings. "Here's what I had in mind for the town square, and Miss Marion's house. Why don't you take them home and see how you can improve on them? Your schedule says you have a study period right at the end of the day. We'll meet tomorrow to go over what you come up with and then go from there."

Three days later, Jake found himself mixing paint trying to make just the right shade of brown for the library scene. When one of the other stage crew members, a senior girl named Carly, started to dip her brush directly into the can, Jake snapped at her, "Geez, don't put your brush right into the can. You want to ruin the rest of it?"

The girl stared at him, shocked. "What is your problem? There aren't enough of those little trays to go around."

Jake sighed. "My problem is that if you put your brush right into the can, then all the dirt and dust on your brush goes right into the can and messes up the color. That's why we use the trays to begin with. Besides," he said standing, and addressing the other painters, "we need to prime the plywood before we do the final color anyway."

Another long-time stage crew member asked plaintively, "Why? We never did before and I've been on stage crew since I was a freshman. This is my third production."

Jake explained, warming to his topic. "If we don't put a coat of white primer on the boards, then the color coat won't soak into the wood evenly. It'll bleed in funny places and look weird."

A few in the group nodded, seeing the logic. Carly still protested, "I don't see why we can't just paint two coats of the brown and even it out as we go."

Jake told her, "The primer is cheaper so we won't go over budget on paint, and can spend the money on cooler stuff. Like some gold trim on the gazebo in Act Four."

Everyone agreed this detail would make a real difference in the set. They got to work priming the plywood boards. Jake took a can of white primer spray paint and began to apply it in neat, even strokes. The can seemed to melt into his hand, and before long he took a gentle breath of the fumes, remembering with a hint of sadness the last time he held such a can in his hand. He felt the mist dry on his fingers and shivered with excitement. Before he could go any further, he heard Ms. Lee call him over to her table set off to one side of the stage.

"Jake, that was quite a little lesson in stagecraft. I'm impressed."

Jake felt proud and embarrassed at the same time. He hadn't realized anyone outside the immediate circle had been listening. "I picked up a few things working with the mentors at ArtWorks. A bunch of them are art students and they've been teaching us about how paint works on different surfaces and stuff."

Ms. Lee smiled. "It looked like they've been teaching you a bit about patience as well. I know Carly can sometimes think she is the only person who ever built a set for this school. It was great the way you showed her how to do it correctly without alienating her or putting her down."

"That's something else I've been working on with ArtWorks, my communication skills."

Ms. Lee patted him on the shoulder. "Well, it seems you've been paying attention. Keep up the good work."

By the time the production was ready for opening night, Jake was surprised to find that he really cared about how the show would go. He had made friends on the crew and cast, and wanted them all to succeed. His parents bought tickets to the show, and from the wings, he could see them poring over the program to find his name. Once the curtain came down on the final scene, his scream joined the other crew members', giving voice to their pride and excitement over a job well done.

Once school was out for the summer, Jake's parents surprised him with a trip to London to see shows in the West End, London's famous theater district. His father said, "Son, I'm proud of the way you faced up to your responsibilities after the unfortunate incident with the auto shop. You've convinced me that art may be the way for you, after all. I hope this trip will give you some things to think about for next year when you have to start turning in your college applications."

Jake didn't have the heart to tell him that he never actually finished his time with ArtWorks. Once he started working on the play at school, his priorities shifted and he didn't think a week or ten days was too much to worry about skipping out on. No one from the program had contacted him or his parents, so he figured they wrote him off and gave him credit for the time he did complete.

Once in London, he went to as many museums as he could find during the days, filling notebook after notebook of sketches, drawings and cartoons of what he had seen. At night, he attended shows of all kinds, whatever he could get tickets to that morning. Theater, avant-garde as well as traditional. After one particularly odd modern show featuring a clown and a parrot that only spoke Portuguese, Jake wandered the city, too keyed up to go back to his hotel. Stopping in a small corner market to buy a soda, his gaze alighted on a hanging sign, "Hardware/Paints." His index finger tingling, he made his way down the aisle. Every color of the rainbow and a few not found in nature were on display in cans five deep on the shelf. Jake could feel his heart begin to race. He quickly brought over a basket which he filled with can after can of spray paint. At the counter, the shopkeeper barely glanced at him. "Artist, eh?" he grunted as he rang up Jake's selections.

Jake puffed up a bit at the suggestion. "Yes, I am. I am an artist."

Out of the store he walked frantically searching for a clear wall space. Dozens of images tumbled through his mind but one seemed to return more often that the others. Grinning to himself, Jake spied the side of a garage that appeared boarded up and abandoned. "No one will care if I beautify this eyesore a little."

Humming to himself, he started on the figure of a woman in a period costume with an hourglass figure, reading glasses and a book in one delicate, outstretched hand that it was the star character of the play he did at school, Marion the Librarian, he was painting. The tune that went around and around in his mind as he painted was also from the show. He sang quietly, "We got trouble, my friends. With a capital T which rhymes with P. And that stands for paint." He laughed, feeling the same sense of freedom and creativity he missed so much. But the feeling left rapidly when he heard footsteps approaching. "Excuse me, sonny. What do you think you are doing?"

Jake turned to face the police officer with a sense of déjà vu. "I'm painting?" he replied, hoping this time if he answered the officer's questions, there wouldn't be a repeat of his last conversation all those months ago.

"American, are ya?" asked the tall man, peering at the half-finished painting.

"Yes, sir."

"Well, here in London, we don't go around painting buildings. Come on. In you go."

At the police station, Jake was allowed to call his parents back in the States. Upon hearing his explanation, his father cried out, "Not again. Jake, why do you think we sent you to London in the first place? To stay out of trouble. It's bad enough you didn't finish your sentence with ArtWorks…"

Jake interrupted, "You knew?"

His mother answered from the extension, "Honey, of course we knew. Vicki called us the first day you didn't show up. We hoped you would admit on your own that you hadn't been going but then you got so excited about the play and so we thought the trip would give you a chance to see how much you'd be missing if you didn't complete your sentence."

"So what happens now?"

"Now you sit tight, and we'll be there as soon as we can get a flight," his father answered.

Two days later, Jake talked to the judge in the equivalent of the juvenile division. His parents arrived in time to sit in on the meeting, having taken a red-eye flight. The judge explained that given his prior record, things did not look good for him.

"You do understand that the sentence that was handed down to you was contingent upon finishing the ArtWorks program, do you not?" The judge looked up from a file before him.

"Yes, sir. I guess I just didn't think a week or two made all that much difference. I mean, I did most of it." Jake shrugged, knowing how lame his excuse was but unable to provide anything better.

"Sentences are for specific amounts of time, young man. They are not suggestions. Your sentence was forty hours over a period of eight weeks. You did not complete that sentence. There is a warrant for your arrest."

Jake didn't know how to respond so he simply nodded.

The judge continued, "Now to the matter at hand. You have admitted the vandalism, correct?"

Jake nodded again, then added after a prompt from the court reporter, "Oh yeah, I admit it. Sorry."

"'Sorry' won't do this time. Taking into account your previous actions in regard to your sentence, I am sentencing you to the fullest extent of our law on the charge of reckless and conscious vandalism of private property. The sentence is two years to be served immediately in a juvenile detention facility. Do you understand?"

Jake nodded, feeling stunned. Two years?

"It is my hope that in that time you will find a better way to apply your creative talents."

Jake smiled a small rueful smile. "Yes, sir. I hope so, too."

space

So, there we were. We had our groups, twelve in all, ready to paint murals on the back of twelve buildings along the Urban Art Corridor in the industrial center of a major city. We had contracted with eight youth groups and the Juvenile Court to get the jobs done. Now all we needed was to determine where this would be accomplished. Our office was fine for administrative purposes but not for coordinating the painting of murals.

Sure, you say, you had the wide open spaces of the corridor itself. But, that didn't take into account the need for paint storage, materials for such a mammoth job, and a meeting place for as many as three hundred kids. There, they'd get their assignments before being transported to the mural sites. When through painting, they would be transported back to the meeting place for check-out. (Record-keeping is absolutely critical on these jobs and required for court-assigned youth.)

Independent space was clearly needed and quickly, if we were to make our schedule meaningful. The hunt for warehouse/studio space was on. I put out a plea to the community, to all members of the SODO Business Association.

A day later, I got the call. It was from Richard, the Executive Director of the Frye Art Museum, a major showplace of art on Seattle's First Hill. They were members of the Association because they used their endowment funds to acquire revenue-producing warehouses in our area. Managing their properties was a charter member of the Association. In fact, the museum's president was elected as one of the first board members of ArtWorks.

Richard's message was short and sweet. "How would you like to have use of one of our warehouses over on Sixth Avenue South, a block from where you want to paint the murals?" Somewhat overwhelmed by his question, presented without so much as a, "Hello, how are you," I said, "You bet!" even before I realized we had not even seen the property.

I wasn't even sure where it was. I soon found out. Monica and I hopped in Ron's car and drove the two miles to the site. We were not disappointed as Richard showed us around. Complete with loading dock, it was large, about three thousand square feet, basically a large room with high ceilings; yes, a warehouse. Up front were four offices. What could be better? It was perfect.

Assuming we were going to have to pay rent, we asked, "When can we move in?" even before discussing terms. Richard provided us with another blockbuster answer in two parts. "How about this afternoon and, no, you don't have to pay rent!" he exclaimed. "All we ask is that you pay a share of the taxes, utilities and necessary insurance, commonly referred to as triple net costs." Without hesitating to figure out what that means fiscally speaking, we said, "How about tomorrow and do you need a deposit, contract, or what?"

The deal was sealed. We estimated the annual cost to be in the $10,000 range, a figure we were sure we could live with. Our ultimate lease indicated that we could be asked to leave with a ninety-day notice should it become necessary to provide the space to a real paying tenant or even for cause, if needed. A fair arrangement, to be sure!

To our amazement, the previous tenant had left several desks and even a filing cabinet. Added to our two desks and another cabinet, we were set. Monica was using her own computer, and it became clear that we needed a new computer or two. In the hallway outside the offices, they had left a time clock for the kids to check in as they arrived and left. This added bonus proved most worthwhile. Record-keeping is necessary when dealing with juvenile offenders, but it was also used for other groups. Some of this information became part of our grant applications. It made for a credible attachment.

After a quick trip to both Home Depot and a local art supply house (both SODO Business Association members and supporters), we were nearly ready to begin life in our new quarters. It became evident early on that we were in need of lockers and shelving. Once again we sent to the Association members for help. A local storage firm nearby had several older lockers the owner had taken in from a customer who was replacing them. We could have them if we could transport them. One of our staffers had the use of a van so the move was pretty simple. Then our supplier of scaffolding for mural painting informed us he had some old shelving. The next day, it arrived. Now we were truly in business.

We now had a space, a great space, mural sites, twelve groups of kids to paint them, an art review committee, a good board of directors, supplies for the summer's work effort, and then it dawned on us. Mentors! We're ready to begin painting murals with some three hundred plus youth and we had no supervision, except for yours truly and minimum staff, namely an E. D., an intern, a consultant and a couple of directors willing to help. We had told the Juvenile Court folks we would have a mentor or supervisor for every five or six kids. And, we did not.

"I have an idea," Sarah, our intern, said. "Why don't we ask the college art departments for volunteers? Or work-study programs within the departments to provide information about what we're doing? Maybe some students will help us. Might even involve class credit. I'll make a couple of calls."

And call she did. Not only did she contact the accredited schools but the art schools as well. Lo and behold, the phone started ringing. In all, twenty young college or art school students and three instructors were asked to supervise a half dozen or so kids as they attempted to paint a mural. Inasmuch as there were as many as twenty-five youth for each mural, we assigned three mentors. The head mentor was chosen based on experience and tolerance factors.

Now we were ready.

Our new studio/work space was only a block from the north end of the Urban Art Corridor. Since we had the use of a van, we were able to transport kids and supplies. The scaffolding company had already installed their product at each mural site. Scaffolding is portable and easily moved with a little brute strength of a handful of youth.

Rules about who can work on scaffolding varies from city to city. In the case of Seattle, out kids could stand no higher than sixteen feet.

We had a week or so to work with each mentor group. We also briefed them on the group providing the labor, so to speak, and gave appropriate contact information. We were especially careful about whom we assigned to the juvenile offender groups. Since this was totally new ground for us and them, we were not sure what might or could happen. On the second Saturday of June, the fun began.

The first mural, the one sponsored by Cutter & Buck, was essentially the prototype. Because it was across the street from yet another SODO member, a major outdoor advertising company, artists from that organization offered to assist in the effort to get it done and done right. They advised us on prep work that was needed on the surface, for example. This training proved invaluable as we started the other eleven murals. They told us that only vinyl latex-type paint should be used, though we knew that already, and they advised on types of brushes, and provided other tips. Some twenty kids and three mentors, joined by three to five pros from the outdoor company, started to work. First, the mural was blocked off in one to two-foot squares, each with a designated color. All of this had first been done on graph paper in the studio, so that when we began, it fell into place fairly easily. Each youth at three height levels was assigned to a certain color. The artists, though frustrated at times with the slowness of the kids in their efforts with a paintbrush, managed to successfully advise and help them. By day's end, some seven hours later, the mural was nearly half done! None of us could believe it. The long and short of it was that this particular mural, an abstract type design, 30' by 18', was completed by the assigned kids, mentors, and other artists in two days over two weekends.

During the next six weeks, all eleven murals were done, and the summer was only half over. We not only completed all the assigned murals, but by summer's end, there would be a total of twenty-three murals, literally glowing on the Urban Art Corridor for everyone to see and admire. The largest was some 30' by 30'. Others, considerably smaller. Several were of an abstract design, others "mystic" in style, still others with some type of message such as recycling. Not one resembled typical graffiti, much to our surprise.

That first summer, mid-June through Labor Day, we had used a total of over seven hundred youth, including over one hundred and fifty from Juvenile Court.

For a Saturday, Monica had arranged for two hundred and fifty youth and others to paint seven murals. All in one day! We arrived about 8 AM to a sea of kids of all ages!. There was a group of Chinese kids from the International District and, get this, a group of a dozen senior citizens from an organization named Dale

Chihuly's Seniors in Art. Dale Chihuly is a well-known glass artist from the area who was very interested in our program. He would later become a prime sponsor of many of our projects. Remember…relationships.

These Saturday seven murals were devoted to a theme of transportation, each designed around a mode of transportation, a bus, a truck, cars, and so on. Perfect for an industrial area of town.

In the many years that ArtWorks has been in existence, there has never been a day quite like that one. Here is one story from that magical day.

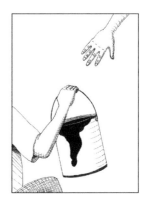

Burnt Umber

I could tell Monica was worried. She had that look. A frown here, a wrinkled up face there, a bit irritated. And, she had every right to be.

This was to be possibly the best mural project ever. Everything had gone so well, until this moment.

"Get over here, Joe!" she nearly screamed. "What do you mean asking a bunch of your so-called friends to help you? Who told you that you could do that, just go out and ask people to help you work off your time with ArtWorks? Why would they do it?"

Joe was a mid-level felon sent to ArtWorks about a month earlier, along with two cohorts. They were members of the "great guys" gang from the Central Area of urban Seattle. He had also tagged several buildings with his gang's tag, thereby marking his turf or territory. That's when he was caught. He and his friends received a rather harsh sentence for a graffiti offense simply because they already had a rap sheet of other crimes. So here they were. Joe had been working with Monica on the design of a new mural they called the "mystic head" only because they didn't know what else to call it. It was in fact just that, the head of a woman who looked, well, mystic, complete with headdress, dark skin, almost

Indian in appearance. Monica encouraged Joe to go ahead with it, even though she had doubts it would get by the review committee. Well, she was wrong; they loved it. Monica assigned Joe and his two friends to the team that was going to begin executing this masterpiece in a couple of weeks.

To fill out the rest of the team, Monica had an idea, an intriguing one. One of Joe's problems was his lack of respect for others, including his own gang members. Joe was the only important thing to Joe, and it became apparent that he could use some guidance.

That's when Monica returned a phone call from the Dale Chihuly School of Art. That was a very important call to return. Remember when I said relationships are key to the success of this type of non-profit organization? Her contact at the school arranged a quick meeting with the powers that be and discovered that Mr. Chihuly encouraged support of organizations like ArtWorks. When asked about ways to help, short of cash, she found out they have a "seniors in art" program. In their golden years, seniors paint, draw, create sculptures, you name it. If it has to do with art, they're there. They also go out into the field on occasion, when the project warrants.

When Monica suggested they collaborate with some teens on the creation of a mural, they jumped at the chance. "Just tell us where and when, as well as how many of us old geezers you want and it's a done deal," one of them exclaimed. Little did Monica know what was about to happen.

Eight seniors signed up to work on the mural two weeks hence.

Okay, she thought. I now have Joe and his two friends and eight willing seniors. Thinking this was insufficient to paint a full-size mural in a couple of weekends, she made another call. This time it was to a community group in the International District, the Chinatown of Seattle. We had earlier directed the painting of a mural on a new building in their area using Chinese elementary students. It went quite well. Kids from ArtWorks had served as mentors, and the degree of cooperation was terrific, not to mention unexpected.

So now she had added five, seven and eight year olds to the mix, a most interesting combination, to say the least. To get the full cooperation of outside groups like these, a small donation would be provided, to individuals, but every group needs something, something they cannot purchase for lack of funds. Truly, a donation often works better than salaries or individual fees.

Armed with confirmations from these three groups, Monica then called a meeting. That's when the fun started.

The meeting consisted of Monica, Joe, the Chinese group director and one child and two of the seniors. Mentors assigned to the project, three in all, were there as well. I sat on the sidelines.

At first, they looked at each other in what seemed like a sizing-up exercise. Then Monica broke the ice. "Hi, everyone. Welcome to ArtWorks. Ready to paint a mural?" After a few utterances barely heard, she continued. "Here it is. This is what you're going to paint. What do you think?"

To my surprise, and I'm sure Monica's as well, the rest of the session went very well. Assignments were made, including scaffolding, and rules of the game were discussed. "Be at ArtWorks at 8 AM, Saturday and we'll walk over to the site. Anyone need a bus pass?"

We were ready to go.

This was the first time during this early period of ArtWorks' existence that we had arranged this type of collaboration. We were somewhat concerned how it might turn out. It could be the best...or the worst...of times. Saturday morning came. We were at ArtWorks gathering up paint, brushes and other items needed for this project. The scaffolding had been put in place earlier by the company donating it. The lift, also donated, was there as well. All we needed were bodies and supplies. As we walked over to the site,

I did a quick head count. To my surprise, we were five over our scheduled allotment. That's when Monica, who also noticed the discrepancy, exploded. You know the rest, except what happened.

After she calmed down, the five "extra" bodies stayed on. In fact, two of them bragged about their proclivity for "graffiti art" as they called it. A total of twenty-one was on hand to paint a mural along with three mentors and Monica. A bunch, to say the least!

Fortunately, we had a camera because some of the scenes proved priceless. Picture this: all eight seniors on the top scaffolding elevation, five of the eight members of Joe's "group" on the second level, and the grade school kids and three of Joe's group on the ground level—all painting away under the direction of a mentor on each level. The first two hours passed. No incidents, little conversation, just painting away in their little squares, which is how inexperienced people do the job. So far, so good.

Then the call came out

"Hey, you," yelled the gray-haired senior man. "You with the bandana." They all wore bandanas of varying shades of red. "Yes, you! Got any burnt umber?" he yelled, emphasizing "burnt umber" very slowly.

"Who you talkin' to, old man?" Joe yelled back. "I've got some brown. Will that do?"

"This gal said I needed burnt umber for this part," the senior said, pointing to the spot on the wall to be painted. "So, I need some burnt umber," he again said very slowly. With that, Joe grabbed a bucket of varying shades of paint and scrambled to the top of the scaffolding next to the senior who apparently needed some burnt umber. Joe was all of fifteen and shouldn't have been on the scaffolding according to the rules, but we were not about to stop him at this point.

What happened next is one of the main reasons ArtWorks exists. A major lesson was learned in the next few minutes. "Listen, old man. I told you, I have several shades here. But no, what did you call it, burnt umber? Here, let's mix this stuff up and we'll get what you need. Give me that can." With that, he began mixing paint. After a few attempts, the old man exclaimed, "That's it! Burnt umber!" I suspect that is the most excitement that man had experienced in several days, maybe even weeks. "Okay, old man. Say, what's your name? It's not old man, is it?" Joe laughed at the man.

"All I know is that your name is Joe and that you're scary," the senior said. "Or, that is what I thought. They call me Sam. Is that okay with you?"

"Hey, my brother's name is Sam."

Then it happened: What came out of Joe's mouth next nearly brought tears to my eyes.

"Hey, old man, Sam, are you my brother?"

With little more than a smile, Sam said, "Let's paint, young man." Afterwards, I saw them talking even more and they appeared to exchange phone numbers.

The mural, one of those featured on the Urban Art Corridor, which in time would contain over thirty, was completed on that memorable Saturday when three groups of people became one, working as a team, with mutual respect.

Joe and Sam became close friends after that experience... like brothers.

Lifting Kids

Here is an example of exactly how proper communication works, or, at least, should work. Whoever designed the Mystic Head mural had apparently not communicated with the other planners at ArtWorks. It is a case where operations and scheduling were not on the same page.

The committee who approved the artwork, along with the head artist or muralist, designated areas to paint: the upper level for the senior group who could legally mount the scaffolding; the middle level was for the assigned youth; and the lower level for the elementary age kids. It was working quite well, until the young kids, via their mentor, realized they could not reach the upper areas of their painting assignments. What to do?

Kids are very resourceful as we all know. Here's a kid trying his best to reach those upper limits to paint what was to be background by the mystic lady's head only to find she could not reach it. Rather than just not do it, or complain to her mentor, she took action.

"Excuse me, sir," she said in a rather subdued tone. "Could you help me?" She was directing her plea to one of the black assigned teenagers on the level just above her. "I can't reach that," she said, pointing to the unpainted wall just above her reach. Rather than ignore her or tell her she was on her own, this young man climbed off his perch, went to her and simply lifted her up. While he had her about three feet off the ground, she slapped paint on the otherwise bare wall until it was fully covered. He let her down, shook her hand, saying, "Good job, kid." Then he went back to his perch. The end of a simply wonderful interlude!

Throughout the rest of the day, similar "liftings" occurred. By day's end, the upper limits of the youngest kids' painting assignment was complete. Teamwork at its best.

It also showed us that all parties on a project need to be at the planning table before it starts, so that every possible outcome can be discussed. In this case, it turned out fine, but there could be other projects where scheduling assignments, design reviews, mentor involvement, and all the other necessary ingredients need to be together to achieve a common end. Sometimes easier said than done.

sustainability

There we were. We had just completed a major mural, one that was to get national recognition. Magazines would feature it, stories would be written about it. We were off and running. Before the summer was over, seven hundred youth, a handful of seniors, and countless hours were invested in the Urban Art Corridor. The twenty-three—that's right, twenty-three—murals ranged from 10' wide to over 500'. Most were done on the back of warehouses or manufacturing plants. Some were done in mosaic tiles, one was computer-generated, one was created totally with aerosol cans of varying colored paint. All were simply beautiful, especially when considering who had painted them; for the most part, kids who, a few weeks, days in some cases, earlier had been in their dorm-style cells a few blocks away.

What next? Well, let's have a party!

Can you believe it? We did just that. Monica had agreed with the powers that be in City Hall to throw a party for these kids, sponsors and anyone else who had participated in this remarkable achievement.

We asked a local restaurant for the food (donated) and asked the kids to come up with a band. We located a venue in an old church in the heart of the area where most of the kids lived and the fun began.

Nearly two hundred of the kids showed up and laughed, ate, danced, and generally had a good time. Most had not even completed their community service time. Yes, this party time counted toward that end, though it took some arm twisting on our part with the juvenile authorities.

Monica wanted to make a speech and talk to the kids about their accomplishments, but I simply said no. This was their reward for a job well done and they didn't need someone preaching to them about morality, juvenile crime and all that. We decided to let them have this time together, making new friends, and simply letting off some built-up steam. At about 1 AM, the doors closed, the music stopped and we looked forward to a new batch of kids to do it all over again the following season.

No Re-offending

"Monica, it's Val. He wanted to talk to you," yelled Dale, a new volunteer.

Val, as you may remember, is our contact at the Juvenile Detention Center, the guy who was instrumental in putting this program together with the criminal justice system. "Hey, Monica," he began. "Heard you had quite a party last weekend. It's the talk of the hall," he said. "Anyway, that's not why I'm calling. We have come up with a most interesting fact about the kids you worked with this summer. While they were working with you on the murals, THEY DID NOT RE-OFFEND! Can you believe it? Not one committed any type of crime that we're aware of during the two hundred plus hours they were in your program. The good judge cannot believe it either," he continued.

"Wow!" Monica exclaimed. "We must have done something right."

How right she was!

What next? How could we use that to jump to the next phase of this project?

The simple fact of the matter was, if these kids don't re-offend during this relatively short span in their life, how can we make sure they don't again? One way was clear. If we can create a program that keeps them working beyond just the summer season, re-offenses will be at a minimum, at least for the kids in the program. That was the challenge.

jeremy

"bum...bum bum bum bum...bum bum bum bum..."

"Hey! Hey! HEY!"

"WHAT?"

"Hey, man, take your headphones off."

"Oh sorry, they help me concentrate on my painting."

"Oh, I see."

I met Rafe two weeks ago. We're partners on the same painting project for the Urban Art Corridor downtown.

"Hey, Jeremy, could you give me a hand?" Rafe is teetering on a ladder with two cans of paint and a paintbrush in hand.

"Yeah, hang on one second." I rush over and take the paint from Rafe two seconds before he might fall off the ladder.

"Hey, thanks, man."

"No problem."

"Jeremy, you're new here, right?"

"Yeah."

"How did you wind up at ArtWorks?"

I know I have to tell someone my story, but I had no idea it would be now.

"Umm, do you have about an hour?"

"Hey, I have the whole day!"

Well, it all started when I was about twelve years old, just a few weeks away from turning thirteen. I lived in the sketchy part of Ballard, you know, with all of the gangs and stuff, but my family was pretty well-off. I went to a good school, and my grades weren't that bad. I was the average twelve-year-old kid with dirty blond hair and blue eyes. My life changed one Tuesday afternoon while my mom was at work and my sisters were at soccer practice. It was just my dad and I, and I was busy in my room doing my homework when my dad walked in.

"Hi, son."

"Hey, Dad, what's up?"

"Oh, nothing." He walked over and sat down next to me. He was acting really strange.

"Umm, Dad, is something wrong?" He didn't answer. All of a sudden he picked me up, laid me on my bed, and he began to touch me. I froze. I had no idea what to do. It was my dad. I looked up to him, but I knew this wasn't right. I finally started to scream, so he got off of me. I looked into his eyes and didn't see my dad anymore, but instead, I saw a monster.

"Jeremy, if you tell anyone what just happened, I swear I will beat you." That's all my dad said, then he just walked out of my room and started to load the dishwasher like nothing happened.

I could not believe what my dad had just done. It was like he became a different person. I was so scared, so I obeyed him and didn't tell anyone, not even my mom or my best friend.

My dad would continue to come into my room on Tuesday afternoons and molest me, but I didn't know what it was then.

"Oh man, I am so sorry," Rafe says, after I tell him. I can tell he's serious.

"Thanks. It was one of the lowest points in my life."

"So, is that it? Is there more to your story?"

"Yeah. That was just the beginning."

Like I said, my dad kept coming into my room on Tuesdays when my mom and sisters were out. I tried to keep myself away from my house on Tuesday afternoon. I would ask my friends if I could go over to their houses or I would offer to mow the lawn for my aunt. She noticed that I was always nervous when I came over, and one day she asked me why I was mowing the lawn two weeks in a row.

"Jeremy, you mowed the lawn last week. Why are you always asking for jobs to do on Tuesdays?"

Well, I didn't want to tell her, even though she was, and still is, my favorite aunt, so I lied. "Umm, I just want some extra spending money, you know, for the movies and new video games."

"Well, honey, you could've just asked for a little money.'"

"Umm, well, I like to earn my money. It makes me feel more, umm, successful." I knew I should've told her, but something inside of me, that picture of my dad's monstrous eyes insisting that I not tell anyone, told me not to tell. Not yet.

I finished mowing her lawn and went to get my ten dollars from my aunt. She handed me the money and looked me straight in the eye. "Jeremy, I know there is something wrong. Nobody mows a lawn two weeks in a row to get some spending money that could have just been given to them. There's something more, and just know that the door to my home is always open and so are my arms."

"Thanks, Aunt Sherry Thanks a lot."

"No problem, kiddo. See you later."

I hopped on my bike and rode home as fast as I could. I had found my way to escape my father's sick behaviors. I ran straight to my room, and I threw open my drawers. I found my favorite T-shirts and jeans. I also pulled out a few changes of boxers and underwear. I stuffed all of this into my duffel bag, and then I grabbed my backpack for school. I was not going to put up with my father anymore, but I still wasn't going to tell anyone.

Then came the hard part. I opened up my backpack and ripped a piece of notebook paper from one of my spiral notebooks. I took out my "battery-charged blue" marker, and I wrote a note to my father.

Dad,

You used to be my hero, but I am not putting up with you anymore. I want to know why you had to ruin my life for a whole year. I hate you. I HATE You. I hope I never see your face again. I am leaving and never coming back because of what you have done to me for the past year. Goodbye.

Jeremy

P.S. Tell Mom and my sisters that I love them.

I found myself crying as I sealed the letter with one of the stickers from my collection. I put the letter in the middle of the kitchen table so he couldn't miss it. I didn't want my dad to overlook the pain and fear that he had given me. I grabbed my backpack and duffel bag, fed the dog for one last time, and walked out of the house, passing my father as he walked in the door, obviously home late from work. He started to ask me where I was going, but I ran to my bike, hopped on, and rode away without looking back. I was thirteen, and I ran away from home and my family forever.

"Oh my gosh, I had no idea you went through so much," Rafe says.

"Well, that's only about half of my story."

"I still have more time, and besides this painting really needs to dry first." He is pointing to the mural of the children holding hands around the world.

"Okay, well, you won't be surprised at where I went after I ran away."

I rode so fast, I didn't even remember where I was going exactly. All I could think about was what I was going to tell my aunt when I showed up at her house wanting to take her up on her open-door offer. I could just imagine what her expression would be and what she would say to me. I almost missed the turn onto her street because I wasn't concentrating on anything...I was surprised I didn't hit anything or run into a wall on the way.

I found myself crying when I rode into her driveway. I don't remember why. I think she heard my walking up the stairs because when I went to ring the doorbell, she was already opening the door. We didn't even have to say anything; she knew by my backpack and duffel bag that this wasn't just a late evening visit. She took me into the kitchen, sat me down, and handed me a box of tissues and a glass of lemonade. Then came the question I had been dreading the whole way there.

"So, Jeremy," she was being very careful about what words she used, "what's really happening?"

All of a sudden, every pressure and fear collapsed. I told her about my dad and how he would come into my room and make me feel so helpless. I told her everything. All she did was sit and listen, with a very shocked look on her face. She couldn't believe that a thirteen year old could go through so much within one year. She didn't even say anything after I finished telling her, but I knew from the look in her eye that she felt sorry for me from the bottom of her heart.

About an hour later, I slowly unpacked the clothes I had brought. My aunt and I set up a couple of blankets on the couch until she could go and get a regular bed. I realized that I didn't have enough clothes even to get through one week of school, so my aunt promised me that we would go get some shirts and jeans in the next few days.

When I went to bed, I couldn't fall asleep. I knew that my mom and dad were probably scared to death about where I was. They always told me not to be out past nine, and they didn't know that I was staying with someone and not just wandering the streets of Ballard or riding a bus to the middle of downtown Seattle. For a split second, I felt like I should have gone back, but then the image of my dad holding me down on my bed flashed in my mind, and I couldn't even think about going home. I had to somehow make my aunt's house my home for the next four years of my life.

"How is it so easy for you to talk about all of this stuff?" Rafe's face is full of sympathy and confusion.

"Well, honestly, ArtWorks has been the best thing that has ever happened to me. Not only is it helping me do my community service sentence, but the counselors and leaders have all helped me grow as a person and an artist, and hopefully I will be able to go to college and study art. I don't want to sound like a walking, talking ad, but I really feel that ArtWorks has completely changed my life."

"What happened when you had to go back to school? Wouldn't you have been in high school by then?"

I was really young in my grade, and I was going to go to a four-year high school so, yes, I was starting high school that fall. It was the second scariest part of my life up to then. My aunt and I went school shopping together, something I usually did with my mom. In a way, my aunt had become my mom, even though I still loved my real mother. She helped me with homework and the laundry. She promised me that I would never have to go to any family occasions that my father might be at.

The strange thing was that my parents never called my aunt, wondering if she knew where I was. I thought they just knew that when I ran away, I didn't want to come back or to see them ever again. That was almost the truth.

The first day of school was the worst day of my life. I got made fun of because of my height (I was really short), and I forgot the combination every time I went to open my locker. Over the first couple weeks, I made a few friends with people I would have never talked to when I was living at home with my family. They were the tough guys of the class. They would go to the back of the gym after school and smoke and drink until they couldn't even talk correctly. I never did this with them that year, but they asked me several times while I was walking to my aunt's house if I wanted to join them.

So my freshman year was over, and my grades were okay. As I started my sophomore year, I lost interest in everything related to school. I began to hang out with those guys after school, smoking and drinking. I never really lived at my aunt's house anymore, I would just go there to eat dinner and sleep and sometimes just to sleep. My grades were all below Cs by the end of the first semester, and there really wasn't anything that made me want to bring them up. I manipulated my aunt into giving me money for the "movies" or "bowling," but I used that money to get marijuana. That was my life. Looking for my next hook-up, and then wondering when I could do it again. It was a regular thing between my friends and me. We would get together after school, and Jamaal, the guy who dealt marijuana, would hook us up with some, and usually we would go through it before it was time for dinner.

Later in the evenings, we would all get together by the dumpster behind the bowling alley and tag different places with our "gang symbol" even though we weren't really a gang. It was one of those other things we did that made us feel like we were living on the wild side of life.

We would do this every week all throughout sophomore and half of junior year. I was sixteen as a junior, but halfway through the first semester, I dropped out of school and moved out of my aunt's house to live in my friend's basement. I thought I didn't need school and that I was smart enough to get a job if I wanted one, which, at the time, I didn't. On top of trying to find more marijuana, all of the tagging, stealing, and trespassing my group of friends were doing had started to become more elaborate and extreme.

One day, my friend came up to me while we were smoking and showed me this crumpled piece of paper. At the top he had written "Robbery Plans" in his scribbled handwriting.

"Man, I don't think we should be doing this." I honestly didn't want to be a part of this.

"Oh, come on, Jeremy. It'll be fun. Besides we need more money for pot. We're running low."

For the next three weeks, we planned, day and night, to rob a store on Madison. We were all high school drop-outs and certainly not professional or even experienced thieves. Finally, the Friday night came where we were going to rob the store. I won't go into detail because so many things went wrong. The bottom line is that we failed because our lead man forgot that when the alarm system went off, the police would know about it and come arrest us.

There we were, sitting in the downtown jailhouse. It was picture perfect. Five high school bums sitting in a jail cell with their black hooded sweatshirts pulled over their heads.

Because I wasn't directly involved in the crime, as I was the lookout, I didn't receive any jail time or juvenile detention. Instead, I was sentenced to two hundred hours of community service. And if you can't figure that out, that is about eighty days of service if I do five hours a day.

"That's why you're here?"

"Yeah, but honestly I am glad I found ArtWorks. I was able to kick my drinking and smoking, and I actually think I have a shot at art school."

"Wow! You really have dreams."

"Well, here I got some counseling. I never knew that all the graffiti and tagging that I did could actually prove useful. Had I not been sentenced to community service, I would still be causing trouble and getting in more trouble. I can honestly say that Art-Works has changed my life. "

"Hey Jeremy…you just spilled green paint all over your shoes."

Jeremy finished his community service hours and was accepted into the Art Institute of Seattle. He still keeps in touch with his aunt, and he called his mother after he graduated with a degree in graphic design. He hasn't spoken to his father since the day he ran away from home. His success, he says, is due to his experience at ArtWorks. He currently works for a major company, designing the covers for video games.

seattle seahawks

During the time we began the program in 1995, with the first mural created following the summer in June of 1996, our Seattle professional football team was seriously thinking about a new stadium. Meanwhile, the voters had created an authority to contract a new ballpark for our professional baseball team and construction was underway. It would open a few years later. But the football team was still playing in the old worn out and very tired domed stadium, which had been state-of-the-art many years earlier. Another vote, another stadium, this time for the Seahawks.

Remember what I said many times about relationships? Well, here it was again. As critical as ever.

As President of the SODO Business Association, I was invited to all of the community meetings related to the new construction of these stadiums. After all, they were side by side, within the geographic boundaries of the Association and were in good standing as long-time members. It is interesting to note that in the eyes of City Hall's planners and zoning regulations, stadium use was considered industrial in nature.

At one of these community meetings on the new Seahawk stadium design and future, a chance remark was made that led to an altogether new future for ArtWorks.

"Hey, Jim. How are you? Are you sorry to see this old dome torn down for your new stadium? It's been your home these many years," I said.

"The short answers, Mike, are, first, I've never been better and second, no, no, no! This place has served the community for over twenty years. Concerts, games, all sports, high school playoffs, you name it, it's been done here," he said.

"But it has to go. Tell you what. I love the mural you guys did for us, that really big one with the players. Everyone here likes it, too. What can we do to keep the program alive?"

I then told him the kids don't re-offend while in the program. He was totally surprised to hear that. As the man in charge of community relations for the Seahawks, he had worked with other youth groups in cities like Portland, Oregon, where they had connections. He made a proposal.

"Why not keep it going all year long? You have a studio now that seems to work. Let's give you a job that will keep the kids working for the next couple of years, work that can be done completely in the studio. We built a new stadium a couple of years ago in Portland where we used some local school kids to create some construction site panels that we put up during construction. Well, our new stadium here is more than a city block in size and we could use some panels, say five hundred of them. We'll pay you $50 for each one and we'll get the contractor to provide the panels. Can that work?"

In a somewhat mocking but sincere manner, I said, "I think we can work it out, Jim. Wow! What a deal! When can we start?"

Fortuitously, this "relationship" yielded a project that resulted in a year-round effort, one involving literally hundreds of kids over the next three years. A few weeks later, truck after truck arrived loaded with 4'x 8' plywood panels. We had some two hundred at any given time to work on, until all five hundred were completed. These colorful messages were then used around the construction site and periodically changed. Themes were pre-approved by our review committee, the Seahawks and their contractor. The panels were so impressive after they were installed that a couple of local television stations asked to do a story about them.

Our record of not re-offending safely preserved, we were off and running. But, the struggle continued.

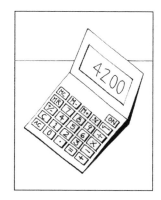

More on Funding

As mentioned, the laborious task of applying for and receiving what is commonly referred to as the 501(c)3 status is a must. Most organizations from the Bill Gates Foundation to the smallest of the small require it for obvious reasons. Once this status is attained, charitable donations can be written off for tax purposes.

Inasmuch as it takes time (and money usually) even to apply, until such status is conferred, many non-profits will use another organization which already has the 501(c)3 designation when seeking funding. That is perfectly legal. In fact, ArtWorks has since done the same for other groups, for a small fee based on time or number of checks, usually a few hundred dollars. The SODO Business Association, for example, would charge $100 per check to administer funding for groups or grants without their own charitable donation status with the IRS.

That administrative detail out of the way, serious but necessary fundraising could begin.

Raising much needed money takes many forms. There is one requirement for any successful fundraiser—persistence. Without that, forget it. Some people simply cannot fundraise. They treat it much like bill collecting which, of course, it is not. It's like going to Mexico and attempting to bargain with vendors for the best deal on that scarf. No one pays full price, but again, some cannot fundraise and ultimately they pay the price. Going into any fund-raising program, find the person or persons who are comfortable asking for the order. Many times it is as simple as arranging appointments or speaking engagements with groups, companies, agencies, or individuals.

Here are a few suggestions for starters.

While the Internet is nothing short of terrific when it comes to researching funding, one of the most rewarding institutions you can visit is the public library. In the reference section of most libraries, you'll find foundation directories complete with descriptions as to what they will and won't consider funding. Depending on your goal—after-school programs, mentoring opportunities, art or other projects— you'll soon discover that not all are equal. Not all of them will provide the needed funds based on your goals. Research will save you lots of time. Most grantors require humongous forms to be filled out very neatly and completely, so that they can be totally understood quickly. It takes a very skillful writer of grant requests to successfully accomplish this. Many schools have grant-writing classes or even give degrees in this area. It is possible that your program can be used as a model or a training exercise if you approach the teacher or responsible department. Sometimes this approach works, sometimes not. But, it's worth the attempt. All it takes is one successful application, and remember, once you've received a successful result, more often than not, there are renewal opportunities.

ArtWorks has, for example, received several project grants from both the Paul Allen and Gates Foundations. We even located a somewhat obscure foundation headquartered in California that only funds after-school programs in Washington and California. We applied and a few weeks later were notified we were awarded a three-year grant that could be renewed for another three years, maybe ad infinitum. In fact, we're on the second year of that particular grant as of this writing.

Again, the magic word is persistence. Without it, grant applications are nothing more than exercises in frustration, and in some cases, sheer panic. But don't give up. As I said, all it takes is one more successful attempt to keep it going.

Most service organizations have charity-type programs or certainly have members interested in helping. Here is an example of what I mean.

I received a call from a woman who was the Executive Vice President of a local bank. She was also a member of the Downtown Rotary, a worldwide service organization that meets weekly in most cases, and attendance is generally mandatory. Virtually every city has a chapter made up of key businessmen and businesswomen, each with its own program. There may be several in larger metropolitan areas. You'll find, for example, that each has its favorite charities, often youth-oriented, like local Boys and Girls Clubs.

So, I was very pleased to accept a speaking engagement for a presentation about ArtWorks at the prestigious Downtown Rotary, one of the largest and oldest in the country.

Subsequent to our presentation, I received several inquiries from members wanting to know more about ArtWorks. A number of members—there were over six hundred in attendance that day—actually presented me with cash or checks. As part of the program, the woman who called me presented us with a check for $2,000. She said later that she had done her homework before the gathering and convinced her bank to make this contribution. I have no doubt that gesture provided sufficient incentive for those also donating then. In all, that one luncheon date netted ArtWorks over $5,000.

But I have also gone to several events that resulted in nothing. That is the price you simply must pay in these days of limited charitable funds. In the long run, efforts pay off, and often in ways you'd least expect.

I attended a meeting of a local Lions Club, which has a reputation for youth projects and support. I did not receive cash that day but did receive an opportunity to make a presentation to a construction company for painted panels around a job site. Don't always expect cash. Jobs and projects are equally important and go hand in glove.

Again, you know your area better than anyone else and have to determine which groups to approach. Yes, you have to make the approach. Rarely will donors come to you. In the case of the bank executive, she was looking for a program and asked a person she knew at City Hall for some contacts, and my name came up.

Whether it is the local community club or an area chamber of commerce, you don't know what the outcome will be. You simply have to do it. One of our staffers knew a person who knew a person whose father was a member of a group called Social Ventures here in Seattle. I didn't have a clue who they were. None of us did. But, one of our staff members told us that it is made up of well-heeled individuals who are looking for ways to give money in exchange for tax advantages. What a position to be in, right? Anyway, we made the presentation at their monthly luncheon. Actually, we asked the person who gave us the lead, to make the presentation. He did an outstanding job, along with a couple of the kids who joined him at the podium. The audience consisted of individuals who had earned their millions at companies like Microsoft and Amazon.com. More than likely, there are organizations like that in your area or nearby.

Here's what happened after that lunch.

Two weeks later, going through the mail, I saw an envelope from an organization we had not heard of. On opening it, we discovered a check for $15,000 from one of these Social Venture folks. With it was a simple post-it note with a handwritten message affixed to the check. All it said was, "Keep up the good work!" The donor's business card was also enclosed. You can bet his name went into our ever-growing database.

Speaking of databases, whenever possible, ask for the membership lists of groups where presentations are made. Often they protect those lists, but many times they will provide them. Databases are critical to fund-raising, for obvious reasons. More than likely you'll have events like the ever popular auction or dinner or simply a direct mail campaign. The larger the database, the better the results, almost a direct correlation.

Then there are the almost mandatory open houses or special events.

First, an example of the direct open house. ArtWorks has moved four times over the years. Since we rely on donated space, that problem goes with the territory. But it can become an opportunity as well. We use our database, contacts for free or donated food and beverages, press releases and whatever else might result in more bodies, to fill the house over a couple of hours, usually a weekday, in the later afternoon. Here's what happened at one of these open houses:

I didn't know who he was. As it turns out, he saw a small item in the newspaper about the open house for this group who painted murals on the Urban Art Corridor. Well, this guy visited the Corridor, liked what he saw and that was that. A few weeks later, we received a call from Philadelphia, from a foundation with a name that sounded familiar. Sure enough, it was the name of the person who had attended the open house. It seems this person's aunt has a foundation in Philly that provides funds based on recommendations just like this one, from her nephew who worked in Seattle. The person on the phone wanted to verify a few things (501(c)3 number, for example), before he could send us the check for $10,000. That was pretty cool, but what happened later was even better. Every year for the past nine years, we have received a similar amount from that foundation. On a business trip a few years after that first donation, I had an occasion to be in Philadelphia, so I decided to drop in to say hello. It was a simple office in the downtown area, very unpretentious. The visit went well. I made it a point not to ask for anything but simply to talk about our program.

Another example is an "event" held in honor of ArtWorks by one of our main sponsors and early landlords, a major museum in Seattle. Literally hundreds showed up to hear our story, from key government leaders to staffers and kids. They also got a chance to see some terrific art on display at this really fine museum. Again, people would come up to us and give us cash, or at the very least, names and addresses. I figure we added some two to three hundred names to our database, not to mention strengthened our relationship with the museum that one evening. It's often hard to quantify results of events like this. Suffice it to say, they usually work in a positive way in the long run.

There have been times when, as I have said, we were struggling financially, times when we wondered if we could make payroll or pay our taxes or buy necessary supplies for projects. Relationships created as a result of various events provide sustainability in the non-profit world, particularly when government has limited resources.

One of those days where we could possibly fail to meet payroll costs occurred about three or four years into the project. What to do? Quite literally, the program could not survive another week if we did not come up with $5,000. One of the long-time members of the Association and early contributor to the program was the Seattle Mariners organization. I thought I'd give it a shot, try to make up the funding necessary to keep the doors open by going to my main contact. I did, over coffee one morning, and later that day, I picked up the check. Not only did I get the much needed funding, we ultimately put together a program that involved a player who would take kids to games, help them meet other players, make visits to the dugout and provide other fun amenities that I hadn't even asked for.

Remember…relationships!

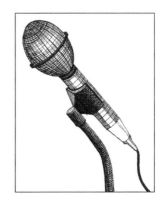

Angela

The fulfillment that Angela felt in that moment was overwhelming. The opposing team's goalie was still lying in the grass, overcome with a wave of defeat at missing the ball. Angela knew that she had scored the game-winning goal, and from the sound of things, everyone else knew it, too. The home side of the soccer field was bursting with fans whose painted faces were aglow. Her teammates ran up to her in one gigantic group hug. She wondered what could possibly make her any happier.

When things settled down a little, she turned toward the crowd. She instantly found her family. Her six-year-old twin sisters, Jasmine and Amelia, were screaming with the multitude, hands over their ears as if to stifle the hustle and bustle of everyone else in the stadium, or perhaps to muffle the sound of their own shrieks. Mama and Papa were looking right at her, and she was sure that their attention had been on no one else for the entire game. Each face was dominated with a huge grin, her father's being especially large.

Angela had always been a daddy's girl. She secretly credited all of her success to her Papa. When she made the varsity soccer team her freshman year, when she won first place in the high school science fair, when she was given the solo part she had been longing for in the chamber choir at church... she did it all just to see her father's pleased face.

She turned back to the girls on the field. They had surrounded her, and, without her noticing at first, started to chant her name: "Angela, Angela, Angela..." She felt a surge of excitement as they picked her up and carried her to the middle of the field, the way a mass of rowdy fans at a concert lifts the lead singer off the stage and sends him over the bellowing mob.

Bouncing upon the shoulders of her soccer team, Angela felt something poking at her side. It was too narrow and dull to be a hand, and after a while it started to hurt. She arched her head back in time to see her family waving at her before the scene blacked out entirely...

Angela treasured the few precious moments before she woke up completely and recognized exactly where she was. She remembered very little of the dream she'd just had, but knew it had been a great one. She woke up in a good mood, but that quickly changed when she realized that a man was thrusting the end of a broomstick at her side.

"Rise and shine, little girl," the man said in a gruff tone. "You've had your rest, now let me go about my business."

She recalled now falling asleep on the front steps of a little marketplace in town. She could only assume that this man was the owner of the shop. He was fairly pleasant in comparison to the others she had had to deal with lately, but she still felt upset at his tone of voice.

Angela apologized.

"Don't worry about it. Why don't you go on home now?" Angela didn't want to go into detail about her complicated living situation. She replied with a weak "Yes, Sir."

It was barely light out, but she knew that she should stay awake for the rest of the day. As she walked away from the man, she began to remember the dream she'd had the previous night. It was a scene from about three months ago at the soccer finals, one of her last memories of her family.

Her father had always come to pick her up from soccer practice after he got off work. On the car ride home, while they were stuck in the bustling Seattle traffic, she would tell him about her day and he would listen intently, absorbing every word. The both of them looked forward to these daily trips. But her father decided that, in celebration of Angela's superb performance in the soccer game the night before, they could do something special. He planned a surprise party for her. He got off work early and packed up the whole family in the car. After picking up Angela, they headed out to dinner to celebrate, but on the same route that they had driven countless times before, they were struck head-on by another car. The parents were killed instantly, along with the driver of the other vehicle, and the passenger of the car behind them. The girls hung on a little longer, but help didn't come in time to save them. They died before the ambulance even arrived on the scene.

Angela knew that it was an unavoidable tragedy, but she couldn't help but wonder if she hadn't played so well that night, or better yet, if she had never joined soccer to begin with, if that could have saved them. She pondered "what ifs" so often that her grades dropped, and she completely ignored choir practice. She didn't want to do anything; she especially wanted to forget about soccer. She quit the team and gave away her gear. She tried to erase soccer from her mind completely.

After the accident, she spent all of her time at her grandparents' fancy house in the nice part of town. Whenever she'd visited in the past, she dressed up in her Sunday best and paid careful attention to her sisters to make sure they didn't break anything expensive. She had always felt uncomfortable there, and this time was no different.

Two weeks after the crash, Angela's grandparents expected her to bounce right back. They sat her down and told her that from now on she would attend school, choir practice, and soccer training regularly. They had also hired a psychiatrist, a woman with whom Angela was to meet at least twice a month. They were kind but firm as they explained that they knew she would not be happy at first, but that all of this was for her own good. They ended with "It will be this way for as long as you are living with us."

Angela didn't even try protesting because she knew how stubborn her grandparents were. She didn't tell them she wasn't ready to start her life over. She didn't make it known that she couldn't even think about what happened to her family, let alone talk to an outsider about it. She simply sat through their lecture, packed her things later that night, and snuck out her bedroom window while they were sleeping. And she'd been living on the streets ever since.

And now, as she sat on a bench in a park on what had turned into a bright summer day, she closed her eyes and tried to picture the dream she'd had. It embellished reality, as most dreams do. She had never been carried out onto the field by her teammates, and the stadium wasn't nearly as full, but none of those details mattered. She focused on the faces of Jasmine and Amelia, acting silly, yelling out loud and sticking their tongues out at each other, Papa with his arm around Mama, both of them smiling at the daughter who had just scored the winning goal. It was a glorious moment.

When she opened her eyes again, the sky was dark. She looked up at a clock tower; the numbers glowed 1:11. It was already early the next morning! She didn't even remember falling asleep, and was surprised that nothing had woken her up during the day. Her stomach growled. From her backpack, she grabbed the bag of Doritos she had stolen from a gas station a few nights before. While searching for her water bottle, she grazed a can of spray paint.

She ate enough chips to sustain her for a while and set off for the place where she had slept the previous night, where that man had so impolitely disturbed her wonderful sleep. With the can of paint, in her favorite color, lime green, she wrote her signature on the front door. Her writing had improved very much since the first time she ever marked a building. It took a lot of practice, but now she could do it in the most aesthetically pleasing way possible.

She finished rather speedily and wanted to add more pictures, doodles, and whatnot—but decided against it. The sole point of her painting buildings was to let people know that she had been there, even if no one knew who "she" was. Keeping it simple was the only thing that set her tag apart from many of the others. And it seemed that people noticed. Angela was so pleased one day when she passed by one of the places she had tagged and heard a young boy tell his mother that he had seen that same thing on a building downtown. "It's the exact same one! It was the same color and everything, Mommy!" He was so excited, and Angela had to resist the urge to brag to him that she was the one who made it that way.

She put away the can and took another handful of chips. She wasn't tired anymore and didn't feel like trying to sleep, despite the dark sky and dead streets. She chose to just wander around aimlessly until the sun came up. It's not as if she had anything else to do.

She walked for an hour or so. From the neglected railroad tracks and the buildings that took up entire blocks, she knew that she had entered the industrial part of town. Though she could barely see anything in the dim glow of the streetlight, she was entranced by the graffiti on the sides of the huge structures. The walls were like Seattle's gigantic guest books, and Angela loved what people recorded in them for the entire city's residents to notice.

One wall in particular caught Angela's eye. On it was a collage of dozens of separate tags and drawings. To her, this was no act of vandalism; this was a magnificent form of art, a mural that beautified the city. As she got closer, she found an empty space nearly at chest level, the perfect size for her signature. Her heart raced as she realized that she could be a part of something in which so many people had been involved.

She snatched her paint can and smiled as she saw her little mark tie the entire wall together. She took extra time making it look perfect. When it was finished, she stepped back, pleased. She only wished there was more light for her to adore it by.

Suddenly, there was more light, a single ray that penetrated the deep darkness. She turned around and had to shade her eyes because of the drastic contrast of the intense beam to the muted glow. She heard what sounded like a low mumbling of two voices and tried to make out what the people on the other side of the light were saying.

"There she is…fell asleep in my office… saw her about ten minutes ago…vandalizing my building…"

"Is that her? What is your complaint?"

Angela knew that whoever was coming was aware of what she had just done and was definitely not pleased. And she was also sure that the one asking the questions was the one she needed to worry about. There was no use avoiding confronting them; they had already seen her, and now they were close enough that she could see them.

"Hey, you! Girl!" The two men ran toward her. It was the one who didn't have the flashlight that yelled out to her. "Stop what you're doing! Come to us!"

"Why don't you let me handle this?" said the other man. Black slacks and a blue button-up shirt, an outfit that Angela knew well. He was a police officer. "What are you doing out here? What is your name?"

Angela tried to stay calm and look innocent. She had often heard that when dealing with the cops, one's image is key. Inside she was nervous and scared, but she made a conscious effort to present an aura of meekness. "I'm Angela. I was just walking around, Sir. Is there a problem?"

"Yes, there's a problem!" blurted the first man. He was wearing nice clothes, khaki pants and loafers. His shirt was tucked in. Angela wondered what a man like him was doing out at an hour like this. "You just put graffiti all over my building; I saw you!"

As he spoke she noticed a long, thin scar on the right side of his face, starting just above the brow and ending all the way down by his jaw. Angela thought about what could cause such a scar. It wasn't straight and it seemed to be in a peculiar place. It didn't seem deep enough to have been made by a blade at all, in an operation or otherwise. The man must have seen her staring at it because he turned his head the other way, moving so that his right side was in the dark.

"Excuse me, Sir. I know you are upset, but I'm going to need you to remove yourself from this conversation. There will be no outbursts like that, do you understand?" The officer was stern, and the man sulkily but obediently stepped back. The officer apologized and went on. "This man says he saw you vandalize his property and we got an anonymous call that agrees with his story. I am going to have to take you into custody." And with that, the officer and the angry man with the scar escorted her to the police car.

The whole booking process went by quickly, though to Angela it felt like an eternity. She had to tell complete strangers things that she hadn't even mentioned since her family died. She felt lonely and depressed. For lack of other resources, she made her phone call to her grandparents. They sounded very relieved when they found out that she was okay, and, despite her sheepish tone of voice, they didn't seem vexed at all when they found out what she had done. They were over within minutes, which was impressive, given the hour. Angela had been picked up, at about three o'clock in the morning, so by now it was barely five A.M.

She was grateful to see her grandparents enter the room she was in, lawyer in tow. She was confused; her "representative" as the lawyer called himself used what Angela was convinced was another language. She simply nodded. She was relieved when the man, Daniel Taramoto, began his next sentence with "In other words…"

Mr. Taramoto explained that even though this was Angela's first offense, the officers who picked her up recognized the mark she made on the building and were seeking harsher punishment.

"They have matched it to several others all over the city. Do you remember making any other markings like the ones you made this morning?" Mr. Taramoto inquired.

Angela thought this was a good a time as any to be honest. "I made them all."

The lawyer seemed discouraged. "Well, that's not the answer I expected. This makes things a little more complicated." He spoke softly with her grandparents for a moment, then excused himself from the room.

"Where is he going?" Angela tried not to panic. Having no experience with the judicial system, she had to put her trust in the hands of her lawyer, who had just left her.

"He's just gone to talk to the judge," her grandmother reassured. "He said he had assumed that you just copied the tag from someplace else, and now that he knows you've done it before, there are some other things that must be discussed."

Angela was too anxious and too exhausted to question what her grandmother was saying. She felt more helpless now than ever. She wished that she could just press some kind of fast forward button and be through with this whole proceeding.

A little while later, Mr. Taramoto reentered the room. Like most of the people she had met today, he spoke *about* her, never *to* her.

"I have talked things over with the judge. It appears that Angela's offenses are worthy of a hefty sentence. Now, we took many things into consideration when choosing how she will pay back her debt to society. We talked about putting her in a juvenile facility…"

At this, everyone in the room looked up. Angela's eyes widened, and she felt tears behind them. She looked at her grandparents who had already started crying. A wave of relief came over the room at the lawyer's next words:

"But we decided against it. Not only was Angela compliant with the officers who picked her up, but from what you have told me she sounds like a pleasant and clever young woman. Considering the recent situation with her family, we thought it best to opt for a less severe punishment. It was decided that Angela will serve two hundred community service hours. Now that may sound a little steep, but all parties involved have decided that this is for the best. Now, instead of having her do traditional service work, such as city beautification and the like, there is this organization called ArtWorks." He went on to explain what ArtWorks does. "Here is the form saying that you understand Angela's sentence and agree to allow her to participate in the program."

Mr. Taramoto shoved a pile of documents and files at Angela's grandparents. They eyed the papers cautiously, as any smart contract-signer would, and eventually did something that Angela never would have predicted. "Angela," her grandfather spoke, "how do you feel about all this?"

Was this real? Was he actually asking for her opinion? She didn't know whether he was sincere or just testing her, but from this simple inquiry it seemed that her grandparents had changed so much since she had run away. She smiled for the first time in days despite the guilt she felt. She said that she would prefer to go through the ArtWorks program rather than participate in the less agreeable alternatives.

Both of them nodded and signed the papers. And just like that, Angela was on her way out of the building, feeling much more optimistic and loved than she did when she went in.

The time between the morning she went home and her first day at ArtWorks went by in a flash. Her grandparents were very accommodating and allowed her to loaf around the house as she pleased. They were just happy to see her again, and they were afraid to lose her the way they had before. Angela felt thankful but remorseful for the way they were treating her. She made an unspoken vow that she would try and make her life better, if not for herself, for them.

When she got to ArtWorks on Monday she was nervous and excited. She didn't know what to expect, and this was thrilling to her. When she went in, she didn't see anyone, but she could hear voices. It sounded like kids about her age, a big group of them. Angela took a deep breath and gave herself a quick pep talk. "I will make the best of this situation," she recited in her head.

"I promise I will learn all that I can and walk away from this place a better person than I have ever been before." She followed the voices into a big room with bright lighting, chock-full of high school-age kids painting on white canvases and laughing. They greeted her with nothing but smiles.

It was hard for Angela to maintain a positive outlook at first, but she made a conscious effort. It seemed to be working. The happier she tried to be, the easier it was to stay in high spirits. Before anyone knew it, she became a genuine version of what she had been trying to be. She became a leader in her group, welcoming new kids and making sure that everybody was involved. She found herself participating in discussions, volunteering to do extra work, and even staying later than needed in order to finish what she was working on. Everybody adored her, but the people who noticed her more than anyone else were the ArtWorks executives, Mike and Susan.

Their offices were on the second floor overlooking the studio. They had been observing her since the beginning of her involvement in their organization. They hadn't expected a girl who literally just came from living on the streets after her family's death to be having such a good time in this program, not to mention on her first day, but they were certainly relieved to see that she was getting along so well. Her impression on them extended to outside the studio. They had a presentation lined up at the brand new Sheraton Hotel in downtown Seattle. They were planning on lining the hallway with large blank 4'x 8' plywood panels and having the kids paint them as people entered the building. In addition, it was suggested that they have an active participant in the program offer a short speech about their experiences in ArtWorks to a crowd of local Rotary members during their weekly lunch. The executives had one bubbly, energetic girl in mind.

Angela jumped at the chance to speak in front of people. Freshman year she had taken a public speaking class, but had stopped going to school before she could apply any of the lessons she had learned. Now, months later, she was eager to see what she remembered and how she could make her speech interesting and different from everyone else's. She began working on it right away.

Presentation day came in a hurry. Angela woke up early and got ready as fast as she could, trying to ignore the butterflies in her stomach. She didn't mind giving up her Saturday to help set up beforehand and clean up afterwards. All of her friends from ArtWorks would be there.

It took no time at all to lay down the protective sheets on the floor and furniture in the hotel. Setting up the panels was a little bit more difficult, but there were plenty of strapping young men to help her. By lunchtime, everyone was already painting the designs that they had drafted earlier that week. People in fancy pantsuits and neckties walked by, wearing puzzled looks and mumbling to each other. She was amused by what they were doing and how everyone reacted.

Soon it was time for speeches. It wasn't till she sat down on stage that she began to get nervous. She was to be the concluding speaker so she would have to stare into the crowd for much longer than she felt comfortable.

Mike was up first. After introducing Susan and Angela, he gave a brief history of ArtWorks and answered some questions from the audience. Angela felt discouraged when he had finished his speech. He was so articulate and what he said sounded so right; she secretly hoped that Susan wouldn't do as well just to make it easier on herself.

Fortunately for Angela and not so fortunately for Susan, the next speech was a mess. Susan stumbled over her words and had trouble keeping to the subject. Angela felt bad for wishing that upon her, but it did make her feel a little better.

Finally, it was Angela's turn. She took a deep breath and went to the podium. Remember to smile. Following her teacher's old counsel, she smiled and began to speak. "When I first came to the ArtWorks studio…" Enunciate! "…I was another troubled teen that needed some kind of guidance from someone who cared about me." Look at your audience. She kept speaking as she looked up into the first row at the first person she saw. It was a man in a black suit with a white shirt and red tie with yellow polka dots on it. His kids must have given it to him for Father's Day or something, Angela thought as she raised her gaze to the man's face. He had brown eyes, a few wrinkles, and large nose, all easily forgettable features except for a familiar long scar on the right side of his face. When her eyes grazed the wound, Angela's speaking slowed and became more gradual, until she trailed off altogether. She knew that face, but from where? All at once, it came back to her and she grinned as big as she could.

"I know you!" she exclaimed. The man looked around embarrassed and confused. His colleagues snickered at him as she continued. "You own a building in the industrial part of town, right?"

She waited for him to nod in the affirmative before she went on. "I tagged your building! That's why I'm here! It's all your fault!" And with this she broke into a hearty laugh that spread through the entire conference room. Everybody in the place smiled and listened more closely to her as she told them her story. When she finished her oration, they cheered especially loud.

She looked for the man with the scar after the speeches were over. She didn't know what she would say, but she felt it was necessary to at least introduce herself. She found him rather quickly, considering the size of the crowd, but she could barely get a word out before he started to speak, clearly but rapidly nonetheless.

"I am so sorry that I was so callous to you when we first met. It was late, and I was tired. And I want to say that your speech was inspirational. It really was. I have to go, but please take this." He opened his checkbook and scribbled down a check made out to ArtWorks. "I wish I could catch up with you, but I have an important meeting to go to across town and I have to leave now. Thank you!" He hugged her and left.

She was disappointed that she didn't get to say anything to him, but she didn't have time to feel glum. People were crowding around her by the dozens, writing checks and handing her cash by the fistful. She was so overwhelmed by the crowd's reaction. People were chattering all at once, and it was hard to hear the things people were saying to her, but she nodded and smiled all the way through.

When the mass cleared and all the guests had left Angela was left standing in the middle of the room with so much money in her hands that she could barely hold it all. She looked over at Mike and Susan who were smiling hugely at her. She was reminded of her dear parents in that moment, but she wasn't sad in the least. Her tears were those of joy and contentment. The executives came over to help her collect herself and the three of them counted the money. Altogether they had collected over five thousand dollars.

After clean-up duty was over, Angela took a minute to reflect on how much she had grown and in such little time. It was difficult to believe that at one time she was a little girl who was too stubborn to accept the changes in her life. And now she had turned into a young woman who had her whole life ahead of her.

She walked out the elaborate doors of the hotel and headed back to the ArtWorks studio. When she got there she noticed some of the kids hanging out in the parking lot behind the building. A soccer ball was sitting idly in the corner of the lot.

"Do you want to play?" one boy asked.

Angela smiled and looked longingly at the ball. She hadn't played soccer since the accident, and she wasn't sure if her tattered spirit could handle taking it up again. She closed her eyes, saying a silent prayer, her first in months. As she did, her heart began to beat faster, and she knew that she was ready.

"Yeah, I do," she replied and rushed toward the boy. As she did, her chest swelled with happiness, a sensation that, for Angela, was long overdue.

Communication as a Fund-raising tool

Communications take many forms, from the simple press release announcing new projects or staff appointments to feature articles about programs or individuals (the media love success stories involving youth, particularly of the at-risk variety). Often, simple mentions lead to greater opportunities—we had a story in *Time* magazine for example, as a result of a local story. A person who has expertise in public relations can provide professional assistance when it comes to fund-raising. But, as with those who can ask for the order, so to speak, it takes a particular type to be effective. Once that person is discovered, take full advantage. He or she can also create the various pieces necessary to make these programs a success: creatively designed brochures, well-written stories, in-depth interviews resulting in stories, and the list goes on.

I've mentioned staffing earlier but you might now realize that special abilities and skills are essential to long-term programming and ultimate success. More often than not, they are accomplished by yourself, spouse, neighbor, or anyone willing to help. In other words, volunteers.

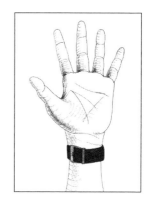

volunteers

Non-profit organizations throughout the world rely on volunteers. Without this ingredient, they simply cannot sustain the level of personnel to meet any situation that might arise, and, believe me, there are many. Getting volunteers, though, is tricky and difficult. They may be friends, relatives, others, especially groups. You must constantly ask whenever possible, at every meeting, during every conversation, whatever it takes, and the result might be one or two people expressing guarded interest. So be it. Volunteers are what makes any non-profit survive. Get used to the high turnover rate, or simply put, the frustration that goes with the effort. However, you must keep the pipeline as full as possible, at all times.

The rewards can be great. We have had wonderful volunteers, and in some cases, they have become permanent staffers. We recruited mentors to supervise kids who could earn college credit, and others who couldn't. They came, they worked, and they usually liked the outcome, not only for the kids but for themselves. Everybody wins…if you can find them and convince them to go to work. Little more can be said. Just remember, you must recruit volunteers just as you must fundraise…constantly. It all goes with the territory.

And, oh yes, don't forget websites, such as www.craigslist.com. It's amazing what you can locate there, from funding opportunities to a desk.

the Board

We've all received unwanted pleas for funds from a variety of non-profits out there. And, in nearly every case, somewhere in the letter, flyer or whatever vehicle is being used to part you with your hard-earned cash, is a list of names. Those names, some you've heard of, others you haven't, that make up the board of directors or trustees as some call them (depending on your by-laws) supposedly make it easier to choose which agency you'll give to. In fact, they may even encourage you to make that all important call for more information. Who knows, you may even choose to volunteer some of your time.

At any rate, as with for-profit public or private corporations, the board is charged with making decisions important to the future of any organization. This certainly holds true in a major way with non-profits. This is because it is often very difficult to get members.

In the case of ArtWorks, we initially created our board from folks who worked with us to get the whole thing started. We realized that this board was only temporary, that a permanent board would soon have to be selected. But how?

First, we simply asked around, organizations we were working with and individuals who served as our main contacts. That resulted in obtaining members who already knew of the program, an important ingredient for a successful board early on. Educating potential board members is not a high priority early in any organization's history. Our by-laws allowed for fifteen, a workable number. Some groups overdo it with twenty or twenty-five, even more. By having eight for starters, of the worker bee variety, we had room to be more selective for future appointees. The fledgling Board kept the program going while educating new volunteers and staffers, including the newly appointed Executive Director.

After we had been in business for awhile, we issued press releases with a plea for interested parties who might like to spend a few hours a month with us. Then, we ran an ad in the local alternative newspaper, the same one that had resulted in an overload of applications for our E.D. From that notice we had many inquiries, one from a CPA, another from a fundraising professional. Terrific! Needs fulfilled. At least in the short run. Many times, members come on board only to leave a few months later, moving on, so to speak. That is simply the nature of the beast. We kept up the challenge for new board members by mentioning that need in every presentation we made, even to such prestigious groups as the Rotary Clubs or the chambers of commerce. I would bring it up at every committee meeting or fundraising interview. The result in a few weeks was a list of potential members, each with a skill we might need. A diverse mix is always good. In fact, right or wrong, some foundations require diversity.

Attendance, policy decisions, employment reviews, including pay, future expansion, programs—all are items that must be of interest to board members if they're worth their salt. Otherwise, you might as well start looking for replacements. Burnout is commonplace with non-profit participation. Don't fight it, or soon you'll be so frustrated you'll go the way of many of them, walking out the door with your tail between your legs and a tear in your eye.

Don't look at this description of board matters as a dismal attempt to keep a program going. More often than not, it is nearly as rewarding as the program itself. The vast majority of boards that I have been involved with have given me more than I have given. They direct programs in a most sincere, direct way, resulting in total satisfaction and, simply put, a good feeling all around. Any other attitude doesn't cut it. Again, remember the magic word...persistence!

Ashley's Mom

"Just get out! Now!" I hear myself scream.

As soon as the words come out of my mouth, I regret saying them, because this time, Ashley takes me seriously. This time, she walks through the door and doesn't even look back.

I start to panic. I pace the hallway, wondering what I should do.

"Honey, there's nothing we can really do," my husband says. "We did our best. And you and I both know where she will be. She'll be fine until she comes to her senses and wants to come back home." Drew wraps his arms around me, and I forget momentarily that anything could even be wrong.

"I don't know, Drew." I back away from his embrace and face reality once again. "I mean, she really took me seriously. I don't understand her! Why does she continue to leave us out in the dark? We don't know where she goes with Jessie and who her other friends are. I worry about her! I mean, if she doesn't tell us these things, I just make up the worst possible scenarios in my head."

"Calm down, Liz. You said Cheryl told you she's headed there, and Jessie's friend is having a party tonight. You know that we can trust Cheryl and Dave, right? Everything will be fine."

"I better go get dinner on the table." In the kitchen, I flip on the light switch. Already, the bright lights and the smell of spices calm my nerves. From the refrigerator, I pull out a head of romaine lettuce, some lemon juice, and some uncooked bacon.

"We are definitely having salads tonight!" I shout up to Drew, who just chuckles to himself. In my household, salads always help my nerves, and tonight, salad sounds perfect.

After dinner, Drew and I talk about what we can do. Ashley has taken a rebellious turn. Everything we do seems to offend her, especially having to baby-sit. Our son Daniel is an angel sent from God, and Ashley loves him with all her heart. But she accused us of having him without really wanting her. Part of that is true: we didn't want a baby when I got pregnant with Ashley. Of course I loved her the minute she was born. Now I can't imagine our life without her. It's just lately I have no idea how to handle her.

I was just like her when I was fifteen. My parents were different, though; they left me alone. They couldn't care less where I was, what I did, or who I was friends with. I learned to take care of myself at a very young age, and vowed never to let that happen to my children. So I always ask Ashley about everything, but she only gives me one-word answers like, "Fine" or "Good" or just "Out." I turned to Jessie's parents, because, unlike Ashley, Jessie has a good relationship and trust with her mother, which I envy. I feel because of their relationship Jessie knows what the right choices are, whereas I never know if Ashley is choosing the right thing or not.

Ashley thinks that she isn't loved as much as Daniel. I feel so bad about this. With Daniel, I know how to be a better mother. Whatever I did to Ashley to make her not trust me, I really wish that she would just take ten minutes out of her "busy" life to tell me what's wrong and how I can help. Ashley is a smart girl, I know that much. My concern is that boy that Jessie is going out with and his friends. They drink and party too much. When Cheryl told me that's where Ashley was going tonight, my stomach leaped into my throat.

After a sleepless night, I call Cheryl to see if everything is okay. She says the girls got home around two, completely sober. Both girls are still sleeping. Relief sweeps over me.

"So they came home last night and everything was fine?" I ask Cheryl.

"Don't worry so much. I love Ashley like my own daughter. I would never let anything happen to her."

I smile. "Oh Cheryl, I don't know what to do. Ashley refuses to tell me anything and of course then I lose my temper which drives her away even more." I let out a heavy sigh.

"Well, Jessie tells me everything and I know they are just being teenagers. I promise to call if I suspect anything funny." She pauses and in the background I hear their youngest daughter, Sarah, screaming Jessie's name.

"It looks like you have got yourself a handful there."

"Oh I forgot to mention, today is Sarah's recital, and Ashley is going to hang out with Jessie's friend…what was his name… oh I don't remember, but he's one of Byron's friends." I feel the panic start.

"Don't worry, I know Spencer. You just go have a relaxing weekend, and I'll be in touch if there are any problems."

"I'll try to lighten up. You have a good weekend and thank you so much for helping me with Ashley. You truly are a godsend. 'Bye." I hang up the phone and walk into the living room where Drew is on the floor playing with Daniel.

"I told you everything would be fine," he says without even looking up.

"I just have to make sure, I mean, she doesn't tell us anything anymore."

"What happened?" Drew looks up. The reassurance on his face immediately calms me down. I walk over and pick up Daniel, his little body comforting me. I rock him slowly back and forth, and in our silence, he falls asleep against my chest.

"They went to Byron's party last night, they didn't get drunk, they came home at a somewhat normal hour, and they slept in until about an hour ago."

"See, I told you Cheryl would have everything under control." I walk into the adjoining room and put Daniel in his crib for his nap. "I worry so much about her, even when I know what's going on. It's just…I don't want her to make the same mistakes I made."

"Honey, I know what you mean, but we need to give Ashley some room. This weekend will be good for her, and as soon as she comes home then we can start fresh again. Okay?" He encloses me in a warm embrace.

It is hard for me not to worry. When I was about sixteen, I made some really bad choices. I went to parties and got drunk more times then I can count. I almost got pregnant numerous times. I did drugs, I smoked cigarettes, I was a screwed-up kid. I didn't have anyone to rely on, and no one told me what was good and bad. My parents were ignorant of what I was doing or simply didn't care. They never waited up for me at night and sometimes I spent the night with whichever boy I happened to be dating. I don't want that to happen to Ashley. Ashley is still so innocent and I want her to stay that way as long as possible. I want her to have goals in life; I want her to succeed, like I never did. But Ashley can't see why I am so hard on her. I never told her about my real past.

This afternoon, I call Cheryl and we plan to go for dinner that night. I really need to talk about Ashley and get advice. We meet at our favorite Mexican place, and after the margaritas arrive, Cheryl drops the bomb. "Liz, I love Ashley like my own daughter, but I don't think it's right that she runs away like that," says Cheryl sounding oddly calm.

"Right now I think the best thing would be to have Ashley come home. Try to talk it out. Let her know how much you love her." Cheryl takes both of my hands in her own and gives them a little squeeze. "I am always here to help you, remember that."

"I don't know what I would do without you."

The next day, I get a call from Cheryl. She's talked with Jessie. "Liz, I am so sorry, but Jessie got furious and now I found out that Ashley took her stuff and left. Jessie won't tell me where she went. Is Ashley there?" I feel my stomach drop. Ashley is gone. Then I get angry. I mean, how could she be so stupid? How do I know that some man didn't grab her and rape her, or that she isn't lying in a ditch where no one will ever look to find her cold, dead body? I immediately remember the park where I used to take her when she was little. Its community center has lockers and couches, and all the workers there know Ashley by name.

As I grab my coat, I turn to Drew. "Ashley ran away from Jessie's but I think she may be at the community center. You stay here with Daniel. I'll call you."

"Drive safely and try to stay calm."

In the community center, I ask if Ashley was there. The guy at the counter nods yes, but says she has already left. He points to a locker over by the gym. I go over and open it, wondering what to do with her stuff. If I take it she will freak out, but I can't just leave it here. I go back to the guy at the desk. He says it's okay if I call every few hours to check up on her.

But I don't need to call again, because as soon as I get home I get a call from the police. They caught Ashley doing graffiti on a building downtown, alone. When they put her on the phone, I am furious. Graffiti? What was she thinking? Who is she hanging out with? I am so angry. I almost miss her choked words, saying that she is sorry. She is sobbing so hard she has to pause for a breath.

I call the neighbor to watch Daniel. Drew and I go downtown as quickly as possible. We find Ashley at a table talking to a judge, with a lawyer next to her. The judge tells us that Ashley has been vandalizing property, but since she is a first-time offender, she is being sentenced only to community service.

We ride home in silence. I try to figure out a way I can talk to her without exploding with anger. Ashley sits in the back seat crying. As soon as we step out of the car Drew is the first to talk.

"Ashley, what did you think you were doing?"

"I'm sorry," Ashley says looking at her shoes.

"Sorry isn't going to cut it! How did you get a hold of spray paint? Who introduced you to that great idea? We know Jessie doesn't sink so low as to destroy someone else's property!" I yell.

"Yeah, well, Jessie isn't as messed up as me, because at least her parents CARE ABOUT HER!" Ashley screams. She runs upstairs to her room and slams the door.

"This isn't over yet, missy! We still have to talk punishment!" Drew shouts up the stairs.

Drew and I sit in silence for a long time. We are both speechless. We never thought that Ashley was going to get in trouble with the authorities. Graffiti? we keep asking ourselves. Where did that come from? How could she possibly see that graffiti was okay? After a long time we decide that she is not allowed out of our sight. She will be grounded until she is finished with her community service.

We eat dinner in silence, only little Daniel making little gurgling noises every once in a while. Afterwards, Ashley returns to her room, and Drew and I watch TV and play with Daniel. It seems like a normal evening, except we all have the same thing on our minds.

Today, Ashley went to school, and then to ArtWorks. What is this ArtWorks? I don't really understand why Ashley was sent there. But when Ashley comes home, she is smelly and tired, and won't say anything to either of us. She just walks upstairs, only coming down for dinner, and straight to bed after. I decide to let it go. She'll talk when she is ready.

It's a few weeks later. When Ashley goes to school, I decide to go see this ArtWorks for myself.

I meet Jordan, a tall, slim woman who supervises Ashley.

"I'm Ashley's mother, Liz."

"I figured. You guys share many of the same features."

"Well, I hope they're good ones," I joke.

She invites me to join her for coffee and we go the coffee shop next door.

I am nervous, almost to the point of shaking. I keep thinking that this Jordan woman is judging me and wondering what kind of mother I am to let my child wander around and get involved in graffiti.

"You know, I don't usually meet the mothers of the kids I mentor. Some of them don't even have mothers. It's sad seeing kids that go through horrible, life-changing things everyday." She pauses and looks at me for approval, and then continues. "ArtWorks changes these kids' lives. They learn responsibility and trust, and to use these lessons in their lives. It really changes them." She smiles at me. I realize that she is not judging me at all. She really does care about Ashley and even me. I wonder what made her want to do this program, and how come there aren't more people like her in the world.

"I work directly with offenders, but there are other jobs, like ones behind the scenes that many people don't even know about. There is so much paperwork and planning that goes into everything that happens at ArtWorks. Sadly, we are losing some of our best volunteers this year because of college." Jordan drops the last few words as if she is just talking to herself.

"Maybe I could help," I hear myself say, in a small voice full of hope.

"Really?" Jordan asks eagerly.

"Sure, but I don't want Ashley to think that I'm checking up on her."

"That'll be fine, because she's starting on the actual painting to-morrow." Jordan beams and continues, "Ashley is such a wonderful girl. It's amazing how much you two share in common. You know how sometimes you bite your lip when you are thinking?" I blush, knowing that it's one of my bad habits. "Ashley does that, too."

We say goodbye and Jordan gives me the number to call to vol-unteer. I'm nervous, but really want to help. Maybe this can help me understand what Ashley is going through.

The next day I take Daniel to daycare, and go down to ArtWorks. A woman named Dolores shows me what volunteers do: mainte-nance, paperwork, painting, mentoring. I decide to take the mentor-ing job because I know that Jordan and I can work together.

At the mentoring orientation, I get a list of projects I can help with, and a list of kids. Dolores says I am one of the few adults in their lives they can trust. "Make these few months in their lives count for the rest of their lifetime. Group A should be here at eight-thirty tomorrow morning, and Group B should be here at twelve-thirty tomorrow afternoon. You will meet with the kids on your list. Good luck."

As I lie in bed tonight, I wonder what kind of teen I will be mentoring. Maybe a gangster, or a shoplifter, or maybe another graffiti artist. How should I act? Motherly? Friendly? Happy? Emotionless? There are questions racing through my mind. What happens if the kid doesn't listen to me, or doesn't trust me, like Ashley? When I finally get to sleep, I have a horrible nightmare. I am Ashley, and I am walking around downtown, by myself, when suddenly a man comes up and grabs me from behind. I open my mouth to scream, but instead of screaming I ask, "What took you so long?" I am shocked at myself, because the man takes my hand and leads me towards a dark alley. He leads me for a few mo-ments and comes back with a brown grocery bag. He motions me to come over, as if he is going to show me what is in the bag. I don't want to know. Inside I am screaming that it is going to be something horrible, like a bloody knife, or someone's finger. Suddenly everything slows down in the dream, and as I walk towards him, the bag gets farther and farther away from me. He keeps egging me on, motioning to me to come there so he can show me what is in the bag. When I finally reach the bag, I slowly look inside. At the bottom are graffiti cans in all colors: blood red, dirt brown, choking blue and grime green. The man motions for me to get into his car. My body starts following him, but my mind keeps yelling no. I get into his green pickup and we drive to a dirty, secluded area. He leans forward and pushes me out of the truck, throws the bag down and speeds off. The place is deserted. I pick up the bag, take out the blood red can and paint a smiley face on the wall. Instead of it being a happy face, it turns into a sneering face. Then I hear sirens, and suddenly the cops are chasing me. As soon as they catch me, I wake up.

I arrive at ArtWorks at twelve thirty. Dolores is talking to a group of kids in the art corner. I do a double-take as I realize that Ashley is one of them. She's wearing a stained, tie-dyed T-shirt, with dirty jeans. Her hair is up and she has a pencil in her hand. Looking so sweet and innocent, she stands out. The kids around her look hardened and street-smart. I secretly hoped that Ashley would always keep her sweet childish face. I don't want her to know that I'm there, so I walk into the office to organize paperwork regarding the new offenders.

At one o'clock, the new group arrives. Some of them look hardened like the people in Ashley's group, while others have Ashley's sweet, innocent look. My assigned person is Michelle, a first-time offender, her crime being shoplifting. I search the name tags and spot her in back, a tiny teenager with long dark hair and dark eyes. She is wearing a Wal-Mart uniform, and looks slightly pregnant. I walked over. "Hi, are you Michelle?"

"Yeah, who are you?" She tries to sound tough, but her voice comes out as a high-pitched squeak.

"I'm Liz, and I will be your mentor here at ArtWorks." I offer her my hand. She just looks at it. I withdraw it after a few seconds. Your orientation will start in a few minutes, and then I'll see you tomorrow for cleanup!" I smile sympathetically. "Everything will be fine. The people here are amazing, and you will have a great time. Do you like painting?"

"Yeah, kind of, I guess. I never really was good, but I love colors," Michelle answers after a while.

"There are certainly going to be colors around here. The murals use so much paint that we will probably smell of it for days!" I get a smile out of her.

"Well, the orientation is starting. See you tomorrow, Liz."

"'Bye, Michelle." This is going to be easy.

For the next few days Michelle and I get to know each other a little better. I learn a lot about her life. She had to drop out of high school when she got pregnant at fifteen. Her dad is in jail for embezzling funds from his employer, and she is being raised by her mom who has to work two jobs to support them and isn't around much. This leaves Michelle time to party a lot. At a party a couple of months ago, she was raped by an eighteen-year-old college student and got pregnant. She never figured out who the guy was. She was tested and she is clean. Who would do that to a fifteen year old? Why would they just do that and leave? Michelle is okay with it now, although it's only been a couple months. Her son Glen lives with her grandma while Michelle works.

She is also going to the local community college and wants to go to Stanford. That has been Michelle's dream all her life. She goes on and on about how wonderful it is and how her father went there and was so successful. She only remembers the positives about him. I don't want to bring up how long he's been in jail, or when he is going to get out. I can't imagine living on like that. But she always has hope. Already she has taught me so much, and her service continues for another few weeks!

One day, Michelle doesn't show up. I'm worried. I ask where she is, and I can't figure out why she didn't tell me where she went. Dolores says I should visit her to find out what happened. If she's skipped her service, she will get into even more trouble.

I get her address and drive to her house in a shady part of town. I walk up to the front door and realize there are people inside. I knock.

"Hi, can I help you?" a girl in a tight, white T-shirt and an extremely short skirt asks me.

"Uh, is Michelle here? This is her house right?"

"Michelle's pretty well out of it," the girl says and giggles as she leads me through the house. "Yeah, she hasn't really moved since last night. But that's to be expected…" The girl giggles again. I realize she is smashed. I can smell it on her breath.

In a back room, a very sickly Michelle is lying in bed. She's deathly pale and covered in sweat. She seems to be asleep.

I try to wake her.

"She hasn't answered in a while, ever since Spencer left, anyway. She's fine, but she's pretty sick. I don't really get why. She used to hold her alcohol so well." The girl goes into another room.

"Michelle, sweetie, it's Liz. You know, Liz. Wake up!" I sit down on the bed and shake Michelle's shoulders.

"Oohh," Michelle says in a weak voice, as she opens her eyes ever so slightly.

"Honey, you had me worried sick! You didn't show up today and I came to check up on you."

"I'm fine, I guess." She glances at the clock and winces.

"Michelle, what happened?"

"Spencer came over last night, and before I knew it, it was four in the morning. Then Spencer's friends came over, and then they left." She pauses again. "Then I got really sick for some reason. Spencer is at the store."

"Wait, honey, who's Spencer?"

Michelle didn't want to tell me.

"Sweetie, I'm only trying to help you. You really scared me today."

"Spencer is the baby's father. I know that I told you I didn't know who the father is…but I do. And he goes to my school. That's why I dropped out." She starts crying. Tears stream down her face.

"Honey, it's okay."

"You don't understand. My baby boy died. A few nights ago. My mother went to my uncle's house for a few nights, and last night, when I put him down to sleep he…" She starts sobbing.

"Oh, my God!" I wrap my arms around her. "Sweetie, do you know what happened?"

"They say—" She comes up for a breath of air in-between violent sobs. "He died of SIDS? I don't even know what that is! Something like Sudden Infant Death. There's no reason for his death! No reason at all! He's just GONE!" She sobs uncontrollably.

"Shhhh…" I wrap my arms around her and try to press her body closer to mine. She quiets down a little bit.

"I know it's hard. Shhhhh…" I keep telling her over and over until she is silent in my arms. Then I say, "I need to go make a call really fast, to tell Dolores you're okay and need a few days off. I'll be right back, with some food, too." I reach for my phone in my purse.

I call Dolores and tell her. She says Michelle can take the week off, but has to come back by next week. I also call Michelle's manager at her workplace to say she needs to take a sick week. They are concerned, but I say she will be fine.

When I come back, Michelle is sound asleep. I wonder how long she's been like that, and why she has a drunk friend walking around her house. I decide I need to help.

In the kitchen, I tell the girl in the miniskirt that she can go home. And that she should take the bus since she is so drunk. She just looks at me and laughs. She says she wanted to leave anyway because Michelle's "attitude" is getting to her. Teenage girls! What is this world coming to? I ask myself.

I clean up the kitchen and make tea and a sandwich for Michelle. I'm about to wake her up when there's a knock at the door. A very familiar-looking boy standing is front of me.

"Can I help you?" I ask warily.

"Uh, I'm Spencer. Where's Michelle? Still in bed?" He looks tired and drained. Obviously the death affected him, too, and my heart immediately softens.

"Yes, she's in bed, and I don't want to wake her just yet. Can I talk to you?"

"Wait, who are you?" This time, he is wary.

"I'm Michelle's…uh…friend. I help her with her community service, too. But I have a feeling I know you from somewhere."

"Wait, do you have a daughter?" He is panicking now.

"Yeah, why?"

"Ashley, right?"

"How…oh my gosh, you are that Spencer, aren't you?" I feel myself sicken. "You're the one who did this to Michelle? She's such a wonderful girl. You ruined her future!"

"It's not all my fault! We didn't know this was going to happen. And Ashley is my girlfriend anyway. I really care about her, and after what happened with Michelle, I have no intention of this happening again, okay?" His voice cracks with emotion.

I made some tea. Would you like some?"

It's been two months since little baby Glen, child of Michelle and Spencer, died of SIDS. Michelle has recovered enough to go back to ArtWorks and finish her time. She told me that ArtWorks was the only thing that kept her alive. She went back to school and is working to graduate by the end of next year. Michelle and I still see each other every other day to talk about life. She needs help coping with Glen's death. She and Spencer still talk, but being together reminds them too much of Glen.

Spencer and Ashley's relationship remains strong. I think he is a good boy, a bit tough around the edges, but good all the same. He really does love Ashley, and as long as they know the consequences of what can happen, I trust them.

Before an ArtWorks' fundraiser I took Jordan aside. "Jordan, I can't thank you enough for watching out for Ashley. I was so worried. She makes me feel like I am such a horrible mother. But I really care about her. She is my only daughter." I realize that Jordan understands.

"You know, I had a daughter too," Jordan says. "She was out of control because her father left when she was barely five years old. I couldn't handle her, and one night, she snuck out of the house and went to a party. She ended up getting drunk, they all left the party totally smashed. My daughter's boyfriend was driving and they got into an awful accident. Three out of the five kids were killed, including my daughter. It was so hard for me. Afterwards I heard about all the things that my daughter had done. She was a drug addict and she got drunk regularly, and partied and, it was horrible. I saw a little bit of my daughter in Ashley and I guess I was drawn to her. But Ashley has a good head on her shoulders, and I know that deep down she really loves you, too. It's just hard for her to accept that she needs you guys. I will always be here for both you and her."

Jordan and I decide to meet for lunch every Tuesday to talk about Ashley and her daughter, Rachel. We share stories, and we cry and laugh, and by the end of Ashley's service we become the best of friends. Ashley, of course, never knows this, because she is too caught up in her own affairs, but Jordan and I stay close.

Ashley grew up and moved out after high school. She and I keep in touch by having lunch and seeing each other at family events. Ashley and I never got any closer, but we have a trust system. We'll tell each other what is going on in our own lives and then share wisdom with each other. In a way, it is as if we were best friends instead of mother and daughter. I feel we owe it all to ArtWorks.

jamaal II

Jamaal woke up that morning in June with a painful headache. He nearly went back to sleep but knew down he couldn't. Latisha came into his room and basically ordered him to get up.

"Come on, big brother. I even made you some breakfast before you get to be a famous painter," she said. "Out of bed, Jamaal. Now!"

After a quick shower and a few bites of Latisha's scrambled eggs, Jamaal raced to the bus stop. He didn't want to be late. In some strange way, he was actually looking forward to his first day on the job at ArtWorks.

He had been briefed the day before by Monica, ArtWork's Executive Director, as well as Millie, the young mentor he was assigned to work with by Judge Carter, along with five other kids. The mural was to be on the temporary classrooms at his high school, of all places. It was part of a district-wide cleanup of selected communities on a grant the court system had received with the help of the City of Seattle and the School District. A total of six separate murals was to be painted during the summer months.

Jamaal wanted the one he worked on to be better than the others. He wondered why he thought that. So there he was, with the other painters, their brushes and cans of paint in little wagons they pulled along beside them to the buildings on which the pre-approved design would be transferred. Jamaal was sure Latisha would be proud of him.

The design includes a futuristic scene, complete with galaxies, planets and stars. Guys (or gals) in their space suits complement the scene as well as a comic book version of their space ship. Pretty far out, Jamaal thought, quiet literally.

He couldn't believe how much fun he was having. And, even more unbelievable, he enjoyed working with his fellow felons or painters. There were three guys and two gals, all about the same age. He even knew a couple of them from school. Since two of them were only there for two months, not three like the others, they were told to try to finish the mural in sixty days, not ninety as they originally thought.

Six hours a day, five days a week, including lunch time. By the end of the fiftieth day, the mural actually started looking like the early sketches. And, by the sixtieth day, it was complete, except for a few finishing touches, as approved by Millie. Once again, Jamaal couldn't believe how he felt about the whole thing. He was actually sorry the mural was finished.

He still had thirty days to go on his sentence.

"Millie, what can I do now? I want to do another mural. Can I help another team?" he pleaded.

Millie looked at him and simply said, "Come with me, Jamaal."

They walked over to a makeshift desk arrangement nearly out in the open, set up by Monica and the staff to manage this multi-mural project. Apparently Millie and Monica had talked about Jamaal having some free time once his original mural was painted. Jamaal couldn't believe what happened next.

"Okay, Jamaal," Monica began. "Millie and I have been talking and we'd like you to be a mentor on a brand new project, a mural in downtown Seattle. You'd have your own team. We'll provide you with the drawings and a list of supplies you'll need, everything to get you started. Millie will still be your supervisor but basically you'd be on your own. Do you think you can handle it?" she asked.

Once Jamaal got over the initial shock, he nearly yelped, "Yes!"

And so it was. Jamaal couldn't wait to get started. He even got one of his friends to drive him to Home Depot to get the necessary paint and supplies to do the job.

His friend thought Jamaal was totally crazy and simply couldn't understand the enthusiasm for what he regarded as a pretty mundane project. Actually, Jamaal had another interesting revelation about himself. He simply didn't care what his friend thought, because he knew in his own mind what it was all about. Whatever.

Anyway, the next day, he started. Within a month he had the mural half done.

But, his time was up. And he didn't want it to be. If for no other reason, he was getting used to having a regular paycheck. And, he didn't even have to steal it!

He went to Monica.

"Monica, what can I do to complete this job? You have given me a team, I got the supplies, and it won't take that much to finish it, even before school starts. Help me out here," he pleaded.

Well, it wasn't long before the job was done. Jamaal was so proud of the work he and his team had done, he brought Latisha, a couple of his sisters and one older brother to come look at it. His parents were working and couldn't make it. He told himself he would bring them later on.

"I did that," is all he had to say to his siblings. They knew, could sense how proud he was. That's when he broke the news to them about his future, at least his immediate future.

"Monica and Millie have asked me if I could work part-time at ArtWorks while I am still in school. I'd be helping other kids and teams with art projects and some other stuff they are planning.

They will pay me out of grants and project money they get. Like a real job," he said proudly.

And, as they say, the rest is history.

Five years later, Jamaal was still at ArtWorks, but now he was in charge of all the projects, handling the administrative tasks. And, he loved every minute. He worked full-time in the summer and part-time during the rest of the school year. After he graduated, he applied for admission to the Seattle Art Institute where he excelled as both a student and an artist. He had found his calling.

One day in the future, he would go back to Juvenile Court, find Judge Carter and thank her for making this new life for him. But first, he had to complete another mural for ArtWorks.

Specific Contributions to *Good Kids* in the form of individual stories include:

Kenny, Terrance and Jake by Amanda Smith
Angela by Michaela Peringer, age 15
Ashley and Ashley's Mom by Sarah Youssefi, age 14
Jeremy by Christen Heye, age 14
Billy by Samantha Youssefi, age 13

Sponsorship

The following organizations provided critical funding early in the process, enabling me to find time to write and coordinate this account of ArtWorks.

- Stuart Foundation
- South Downtown Foundation
- Port of Seattle
- The Stack Foundation
- Starbucks
- Nitze-Stagen Co.
- Viking Bank
- Process Heating Co.

Awards

Over the years, ArtWorks has been the recipient of awards from various civic and business organizations. Among them are:

- Sustainable Seattle – Outstanding Community Leadership
- Seattle Magazine – Best Arts of the Year
- National Asphalt Pavement Association Community Involvement Award
- Association of Washington Business Community Service Award
- NWSource.com People's Picks (finalist)
- Telly Award, Outstanding Public Service Video

Michael Peringer has received awards for his involvement as ArtWorks' founder. Some include:

- Seattle Public Utilities Anti-Graffiti Award
- Seattle Police Department Citizen Appreciation Award
- Non-Rotarian Person of the Year, SODO Chapter
- Pemco Insurance/KOMO-TV Hometown Hero
- Jefferson Award

About the Author

Michael Peringer was born in Seattle and graduated from the University of Washington. After attending Law School and Graduate School at the University, he entered the business world. He started ArtWorks as a result of a grant to the SODO (South of Downtown) Business Association, an organization he founded. Mike's civic efforts have garnered him several awards. Among them are the Jefferson Award and the Seattle Police Department's Citizen Appreciation Award.

He published *Lifeline to the Yukon*, a history of the Yukon River and has authored numerous articles.

He is married, the father of five children and seven grandchildren. He lives near downtown Seattle.

Appendix

Letter from Washington State Senator Pat Thibaudeau
Letter from King County Executive Ron Sims
Letter from Seattle Mayor Greg Nickels

Washington State Senate

Senator Pat Thibaudeau
43rd Legislative District

November 29, 2006

Mike Peringer

The ArtWorks Project is an amazing project that gives our young budding artists an outlet for their art and at the same time helps to beautify our community.

I have always been a strong supporter of this project because it helps our youth develop marketable skills for their futures in graphic design, fashion design and animation. It also teaches them how to curate, hang and market their own works.

Our local arts community has been deeply enriched with this project. In short, I think this project is wonderful.

Sincerely,

Senator Pat Thibaudeau
43rd Legislative District

King County

Ron Sims
King County Executive

December 2006

Dear Friends,

It is with great pleasure that I extend my heartfelt greetings and congratulations to everyone involved in ArtWorks. Serving hundreds of young people each year, ArtWorks is an organization that consistently demonstrates its commitment to providing positive mentoring and working environments for our region's youth.

Our young people are tomorrow's leaders and ArtWorks offers programs in which they can express themselves and gain valuable skills and training. With a mission of "empowering people through professional opportunities in the arts," ArtWorks is improving lives, bringing art to local neighborhoods, and strengthening the foundation of our entire community.

As Executive of Martin Luther King, Jr. County, I am proud to live in a region that values our young people. We are fortunate to have organizations like ArtWorks that take an active role in providing our youth with meaningful experiences and the support they need to become self-sufficient, well-rounded adults and leaders in their communities. As they reach their fullest potential and realize their dreams, they are also gaining an appreciation for community, team work and self-worth.

Again, I commend ArtWorks, its staff, volunteers and supporters for continually motivating and inspiring our youth. I look forward to further witnessing ArtWorks' success in the years ahead.

Sincerely,

Ron Sims
King County Executive

Gregory J. Nickels
Mayor of Seattle

At ArtWorks, inspiration, hope, beauty and wonder flow freely from paint cans coloring our city and changing the lives of so many young people. Nearly a dozen years ago, SODO business leader Mike Peringer saw inspiration on the graffiti-littered walls that lined the busy bus corridor south of Seattle's downtown.

Armed with seed money from the city, he started ArtWorks, an innovative mural program dedicated to empowering teenagers, improving their lives and transforming our community through creation of public art.

The program targets teenagers assigned by the courts to fulfill community service. The public murals instill pride in the young artists and offer them a positive way to express themselves, connect with their peers, gain real-world skills and prepare them for their future.

During the last decade ArtWorks has touched the lives of over 5,000 young people and resulted in more than 1,500 murals at schools, businesses, parks, construction sites and bus stops throughout the city. As for the once-dreary SODO bus corridor, it has been christened the SODO Urban Art Corridor and features more than 50 colorful murals. The vibrant scenes depict the diversity and reflect the history of our community.

Through ArtWorks, kids do more than paint pictures. They discover the power of collaboration, the discipline of hard work, and the satisfaction and increased self-esteem that comes from creating.

"Good Kids, The Story of ArtWorks" chronicles this amazing community effort, documents the resulting artworks and reveals the transformed lives and promising futures.

Special thanks to Mike Peringer for seeing hope in what was once a barren city landscape. Many thanks also to ArtWorks' board of trustees, the teaching artists, corporate and individual sponsors and the thousands of young people who have worked to build a strong, healthy community through art and culture.

May you find inspiration in these pages.

Sincerely,

Greg Nickels
Mayor of Seattle

Good Kids
The Story of ArtWorks

To order: Visit our website www.urbanartworks.org
Call 206.292.7449 or Fax 206.682.1582

If paying by check, please make it payable to Good Kids / SODO.

Send this form with payment to:
Good Kids c/o SODO
2732 3rd Avenue South
Seattle, WA 98134

Name _____

Address_____

City _____ State _____ Zip _____

Email _____
(For gifts, special instructions, or shipping to another address, please attach additional sheets to this order form.)

Please charge my credit card: ☐ *Visa* ☐ *Mastercard*

Card Number_____ Exp. Date _____

V Code_____
(the three numbers following your card number on the back of your card)

Signature _____

Please send me _____ books @ $29.95 / each _____

Shipping and handling ($5.00 per book) _____

Pre-tax Total _____

Washington state residents add 8.9% sales tax on above total _____

Total _____

Thank you for your order. All proceeds go to ArtWorks.
Please allow 4-6 weeks for delivery.